The Don Novels of

MIKHAIL SHOLOKHOV

AND QUIET FLOWS THE DON

THE DON FLOWS HOME TO THE SEA

SEEDS OF TOMORROW*

HARVEST ON THE DON*

*Published together in the original Russian under the title
Virgin Soil Upturned

These are BORZOI BOOKS, published by
ALFRED A. KNOPF in New York

ONE MAN'S DESTINY

One Man's Destiny

and

Other Stories,

Articles, *and* Sketches

1923-1963

By MIKHAIL SHOLOKHOV

TRANSLATED FROM THE RUSSIAN BY
H. C. STEVENS

ALFRED · A · KNOPF

NEW YORK 1967

THIS IS A BORZOI BOOK,
PUBLISHED BY ALFRED A. KNOPF, INC.

FIRST AMERICAN EDITION

English translation © Putnam & Co. Ltd. 1966

All rights reserved under International and
Pan-American Copyright Conventions.
Distributed by Random House, Inc.

Library of Congress Catalog Card Number: 67-11146

Manufactured in the United States of America

First published in U. S. S. R. in 1965 under
the Russian title *Slovo o Rodine*

CONTENTS

FOREWORD

This collection of stories, articles, sketches and speeches, covering forty years of Sholokhov's career as a writer, is drawn from the volume published by the Military Publishers of the U.S.S.R. Ministry for Defence, under the title *Slovo o Rodine* (A Word on our Country) in 1965. This Russian volume included Sholokhov's separate collected stories *Tales from the Don*, which have already appeared in an English translation, so these are not included in the present volume. In addition, certain of the articles ('A Word on our Country', and 'Sunlight and Shadow' in particular) have been abbreviated by the elimination of some ephemeral polemical writing, while a number of short articles and extracts from speeches have been omitted altogether, for similar reasons. Taken in conjunction with the previously published volumes of Sholokhov's work, this volume completes the publication in English of all the author's significant writings from the start of his career down to 1963.

ONE MAN'S DESTINY

One Man's Destiny

Dedicated to Eugenie Grigorievna Levitskaya,
member of the Russian Communist Party
since 1905

In the Upper Don area the first post-war spring came on with extraordinary speed and energy. At the end of March warm winds began to blow from the Sea of Azov, and within two days the sands on the left bank of the Don were completely bared of snow; the drifts which filled the ravines and gullies to the brim began to swell; the tiny steppe rivulets broke their shells of ice and started rushing madly; the roads became almost impassable.

During that unpleasant, trackless season I had to drive to the district centre of Bukanovsky. It was not a great distance, less than forty miles, but it proved none too easy to cover. With another comrade I set out before sunrise. Our pair of well-fed horses strained at the traces till the leather was as taut as bowstrings; they could hardly drag our heavy briztka along. At times the wheels were buried right to the hubs in the damp, sandy loam mixed with snow and ice, and in less than an hour innumerable flecks of white lather were showing on the horses' flanks and thighs and under the thin leather belly bands. The fresh morning air was scented with the smell of horses' sweat and the pungent heavy odour of the heated grease smeared copiously over the harness.

Whenever we came to patches unusually difficult for our animals, we climbed out of the britzka and walked. The half-melted snow squelched under our boots; the going was hard enough on the road, but at the wayside flakes of ice still held firm, glittering in the sunlight, and walking there was even more difficult. It took us six hours to cover the eighteen miles to the crossing of the Yelanka stream.

9

In the neighbourhood of Mokhov village this small stream, which sometimes partly dried up in summer, had flooded its banks for nearly a mile over the low-lying alder marshes. We had to make the crossing in a frail flat-bottomed boat which could carry only three men at a time. We left the horses behind. On the far side an ancient, much travelled 'Willis' which we had left there at the beginning of the winter was waiting for us in a collective farm shed. The car driver and I got into the rickety old tub, not without some fears for our safety. My comrade remained behind with our things. We had hardly cast off when water began to spurt through various holes in the rotten bottom. We caulked the unreliable old tub with whatever was to hand, and bailed away until we reached dry land again. It took us an hour to get to the other side of the river. Our driver went and fetched the car from the village, and as he got back into the boat and picked up an oar he said:

'If this blasted old trough doesn't fall to pieces in the water we'll be back again in a couple of hours. But don't expect us any earlier.'

The village was some distance away, and in the vicinity of the landing stage there was the stillness that one finds, even in unpopulated spots, only in the depth of autumn and at the very beginning of spring. The air was raw from the flood water, and heavy with the bitter scent of rotting alders. From the more distant steppe around Khopersk, lost in a misty lilac haze, a gentle breeze was blowing, bringing with it the eternally young, almost imperceptible aroma of earth recently freed from its snowy prison.

A fallen hurdle lay on the riverside sand, not far away. I squatted down on it, and thought I would have a smoke. But when I felt in my right-hand pocket I was greatly annoyed to find that my packet of cigarettes was soaked through. During the crossing the water had splashed over the low side of the boat, and had drenched me with muddy water up to the waist. I hadn't had time to think about the cigarettes just then, I had to drop my oar and set to work bailing out water as fast as possible, to prevent the boat sinking. But now, furious with myself for my carelessness, I took out the packet gingerly, squatted on my heels and set out the damp, brown-stained cigarettes one by one on the hurdle.

It was noon. The sun was quite hot, more like a day in May. I hoped the cigarettes would dry out quickly; the sun was so hot that I began to regret that I had put on padded military trousers and a quilted coat for the journey. It was the first really warm day after the winter. I found it pleasant sitting on the hurdle, all by myself, yielding completely to the silence and the solitude: taking off my old military ear-flapped cap I let my hair, wet after the hard row, dry in the breeze while I gazed absently at the white, big-bellied clouds floating in the faded azure.

I had not been sitting there long when I saw a man come round the houses on the village outskirts and start walking along the road. He was holding the hand of a little boy, who, judging by his size, was not more than five or six years old. They dragged themselves wearily in the direction of the river crossing; but when they drew level with our car they turned off to walk towards me. The tall, rather stooping man came right up and said in a hoarse bass voice:

'Good morning, brother.'

'Good morning.' I squeezed the large horny hand held out to me.

The man bent down to the boy, and said:

'Say good morning to uncle, son. He must be a chauffeur, like your daddy. Only, you and I ride on a lorry, while he drives that little car there.'

Looking me straight in the eye with his own two eyes, as bright as the sky, and faintly smiling, the boy held out a rosy, chilly little hand to me. I shook it gently, and asked:

'Why is your hand so cold, old man? It's quite warm in the sun, but you feel frozen.'

The boy pressed against my knees with a touching childish trustfulness, and raised his flaxen eyebrows in astonishment:

'Why call me old man, uncle? I'm only a boy; and I'm not frozen at all, but my hands are cold because I've been making snowballs.'

Slipping his half-empty kitbag off his back, and wearily squatting down beside me, his father said:

11

'This passenger of mine gives me a lot of trouble! I'm quite worn out because of him. If I take long strides he has to start trotting; but you try adjusting your step to this sort of foot-slogger! Where I'd take one stride I find myself taking three, and so he and I go along at different rates, like a horse and a tortoise. And I have to keep my eye on him all the time. The moment your back's turned he's running off to wade in some puddle, or breaking off icicles and sucking them for sweets. I tell you it's not a man's job to travel with such passengers, and on forced marches at that!' He was silent for a moment or two, then he asked: 'And what about you, brother? I suppose you're waiting for your boss?'

I rather felt it would be awkward to explain that I was not the driver of the car, so I answered:

'I've got to wait.'

'Coming from the other side, are they?'

'Yes.'

'I suppose you don't know how soon the boat will be arriving?'

'In a couple of hours.'

'A long wait. Well, in that case we'll have a rest; I'm not in any hurry. But as I was passing and saw a brother driver sunbathing I thought I'd come over, and we could have a smoke together. Neither smoking alone nor dying alone is any pleasure. But you're well off, you smoke cigarettes. Got them wet, have you? Well, brother, wet tobacco's like a treated horse, it's good for nothing. Never mind, try some of my strong baccy.'

He took a shabby, raspberry-coloured silk pouch out of the pocket of his khaki summer trousers. As he unrolled it I managed to read the words embroidered in one corner: 'To our dear soldier from a girl pupil in the sixth class of Lebed-yansk secondary school'.

We started smoking his decidedly strong, home-grown tobacco, and sat a long time without talking. I felt like asking him where he was going with the boy, what necessity drove him on to the road in such a bad season; but he forestalled me with the question:

'Tell me, did you spend all the war at the wheel?'

'Almost all.'

'At the front?'

'Yes.'

'Well, I, too, had my bellyful of misery there, up to my neck and higher.'

He set his large swarthy hands on his knees, and sat hunched up. I glanced sideways at him, and somehow I was moved. Have you ever seen eyes that seem as if they were sprinkled with ash, eyes filled with such unforgettable mortal yearning that it is difficult to look into them? My chance companion had eyes like that.

Breaking a dry crooked twig from the hurdle, he silently ran it through the sand for a good minute, drawing some intricate design. Then he began to talk:

'Sometimes you can't sleep at night; you stare into the darkness with empty eyes and think: "Life, what have you mutilated me like this for? Why have you twisted me like this?" And you get no answer, neither in the dark nor in the bright sunlight. . . . No answer comes, and never will as long as you live.' Then he suddenly remembered his son; giving the little boy a gentle push, he said: 'Go and play down by the water, son; there's always something to be found in flood water. Only, watch out, don't get your feet wet!'

While we had been smoking in silence I had been surreptitiously studying the father and his son, and had been astonished to note a circumstance which seemed strange to me. The boy was dressed plainly but well; his long jacket, lined with worn, light beaver lamb, the small boots obviously made for wearing over woollen socks, and the very neat patch over a tear on the jacket sleeve, all revealed a woman's care, expert motherly hands. But the father looked different: his quilted coat, burnt into holes in places, was carelessly and roughly darned; a patch on his shabby khaki trousers was not sewn down properly, but rather tacked on with broad, masculine stitches. He was wearing almost new military boots, but the thick woollen stockings were moth-eaten, they had never been touched by a woman's hand. And I'd thought: 'He's either a widower or he doesn't get on well with his wife.'

But now, as he watched his son go down to the water, he

13

cleared his throat and began to talk. And I was completely absorbed in listening.

'At first my life was ordinary enough. I'm a native of Voroniezh province, born in 1900. During the Civil War I was in the Red Army, in Kikvidze's division. In the 1922 famine year I went to the Kuban to do donkey work for kulaks, and so I came through. But my father and mother and my little sister at home all died of starvation. I was left entirely alone. You could search the whole world and not find one relation of mine, not a single soul. Well, a year later I came back from the Kuban, sold my hut and went to the town of Voroniezh. I started working in a carpenter's gang, then I went to a factory and trained to be a locksmith. I got married soon after. My wife had been brought up in a children's home; she was an orphan. It was a good girl I got hold of: quiet, cheerful, anxious to please and intelligent, not at all like me. She'd known ever since childhood what a pound of anything cost, and maybe this affected her character. To look at her sideways she wasn't all that good-looking; but then, I didn't look at her from the side, but straight in the face. And I knew no one more beautiful or desirable, no one in the world; and there never will be!

'I used to come home from work tired out, and sometimes as bad-tempered as the devil. But she never said one rough word in answer to mine. Kindly, quiet, she could never do too much for you, she went to lots of trouble to cook you something nice even when things were short. You'd look at her and turn away angry; but before long you embraced her and said: "Forgive me, dear Irena, I've been a brute. You see, things didn't go well at work today." And then there was peace between us again, and I had peace of heart. But you know, brother, how much that means for your work. In the morning I'd get up as bright as the sun, go off to the factory, and the work would simply hum in my hands. That's what it means to have an intelligent wife and companion.

'Sometimes on pay-day I'd go and have a drink with comrades. And sometimes it happened that on my way home I drew such extraordinary patterns with my feet that it must have been fearful to see me. The streets would be too narrow for me, and as for the alleys, they were a dead loss. In those days I was a devilishly strong and healthy lad, I could take a lot of liquor, and I always managed to get home on my own two feet. But there were times when I had to do the last stretch in bottom gear, I mean on all fours. But all the same, I got there. And yet there were never any reproaches, no shouting or scandal. My Irena would only laugh, and even that she did cautiously, in case in my drunken state I took offence. She would undress me, and whisper: "Lie on the wall side, Andrei darling, or you may fall off the bed in your sleep." Well, I'd drop down like a bag of oats, and everything would be swimming before my eyes. But in my sleep I felt her gently stroking my head and heard her whispering something so kindly, evidently she felt sorry for me.

'In the morning she'd get me up a couple of hours before it was time to go off to work, so that I could freshen up. She knew I never ate anything when I'd got a hangover, so she'd get a salted cucumber or something else light, and pour me out a small tumbler of vodka. "Get this down you, Andrei, only don't have any more, my dear." Well, what else could a man do but justify such trust? I'd drink it up, thank her without speaking, just with my eyes, give her a kiss and go off to work like any darling. But as God is holy, if she'd said one word of reproach to me when I was drunk, if she'd shouted or sworn at me, I'd have gone on the booze two days running. That's what happens in other families where the woman's a fool; I know, I've seen women like that.

'Before long we started having children. First a little son, and then, as the years passed, two daughters. And then I broke away from my comrades. I used to take all my wages home; I was getting quite a large family, so I hadn't any money to spare for drink. I'd just drink one mug of beer on my day off, and call it a day.

'In 1929 I got interested in machinery. I learnt the motor trade, and took over the wheel of a lorry. I got thoroughly interested and didn't want to go back to the factory; I found life more fun at the wheel. And so I lived for ten years and didn't even notice how they'd gone. It was as if I'd slept through them. But what's ten years, after all? Ask any elderly

15

man if he's noticed how he's passed his life. He'll tell you he hasn't noticed a thing. The past is like that distant steppe in the haze. This morning I was walking over that steppe, the day was quite clear all round; but I hadn't gone twelve miles when the steppe was thick with haze. And from here you can't tell forest from scrub, grassland from arable.

'During those ten years I worked day and night. I earned good money, and we lived no worse than others. And the children were a joy: all three were getting "Excellent" at school, and the eldest, Anatole, turned out to be so good at mathematics that he was even written about in a Moscow newspaper. Where he'd got this great gift for that science I really don't know, brother. But it was very flattering to me, and I was proud of him. God, how proud I was!

'During those ten years we saved up a little money, and just before the war we built ourselves a small house of two rooms, a pantry and a passage. Irena bought two goats. So what more did we want? The children were eating porridge with milk, we had a roof over our heads, we were clothed and shod, so everything was fine. Only I made a mistake about our house. I was granted a plot of land not far from an aeroplane works. If my shanty had been somewhere else, maybe life would have taken a different turn. . . .

'And then it came . . . the war! On the second day I had a call-up paper from the military commissariat, and on the third I had to report to my unit. All my four dear ones saw me off: Irena, Anatole and my daughters Nastia and Olga. All the children were very brave about it. Well, of course, the girls didn't get by without a tear or two. Anatole, he was seventeen, he only shrugged his shoulders as if he was cold. But my Irena . . . I'd never seen her in such a state in all the seventeen years we'd been married. The night before, the shirt on my shoulders and chest didn't have a chance to dry from her tears, and it was the same story next morning. When we arrived at the station I simply couldn't look at her, she was so pitiful. Her lips were all swollen with her tears, her hair was straggling out from under her kerchief, and her eyes were dulled and senseless, like those of a man not in his right mind. The commanders ordered us into the train; but she fell on my chest, clasped her hands round my neck and clung to me; and she was trembling all over, like a half-hewn tree. The children tried to persuade her, and I did too, but it was no good. There were other women talking to their husbands and sons; but mine clung to me like a leaf to the twig, and only shook all over, and couldn't get out one word. So I said to her: "Get a grip on yourself, my dear Irena. Say just one word to me in good-bye." And then she spoke, and every word was broken by a sob: "My darling . . . my Andrei . . . we'll never see each other again . . . you and I . . . any more, in this world."

'My heart was already torn in two with pity for her, and then she goes and says a thing like that! She ought to have understood that it wasn't easy for me to part with them either. I wasn't going to my mother-in-law's to eat pancakes! I got wild; I tore my hands away by force and gave her a gentle push on the shoulder. For me it was a gentle push; but I didn't know my own strength, she staggered, fell back three or four paces; and then she came towards me again with little steps, holding out her hands. And I shouted at her: "Is this the way to say good-bye? What are you burying me alive for before my time?" Well, I had to embrace her again, she was so beside herself. . . .'

He stopped short in the middle of the sentence, and in the silence I heard a gurgling and bubbling in his throat. His emotion was conveyed to me. I glanced sidelong at him, but I couldn't see even one little tear in his faded – one would have said dead – eyes. He sat with his head drooping moodily; only his large hands, hanging helplessly, were trembling very slightly; and his chin was quivering, his firm lips were quivering.

'Don't go on, friend; don't call it back,' I said quietly. But in all probability he did not hear my words; with an enormous effort of will mastering his emotion, he abruptly said in a husky, strangely altered voice:

'Right till I die, right to my last hour, even as I'm dying I shall never forgive myself for pushing her away like I did.'

He fell silent again, and for a long time. He tried to roll a cigarette, but the newspaper tore and the tobacco sifted over his knees. At last he managed somehow to make a twist, took several greedy draws and, clearing his throat, went on:

'I tore myself away from Irena, took her face between my palms and kissed her, and her lips were like ice. I said good-bye to the children and ran to the carriage; I jumped on the step just as the train started moving. It drew away very gently; I had to pass my family. I looked and saw my orphaned children standing bunched together, waving to me; they tried to smile, but couldn't. But Irena pressed her hands to her breast; she was whispering something with her lips white as chalk, she was gazing at me without blinking, leaning forward, forward, as though she was walking against a strong head wind. And so she has remained in my memory ever since: hands pressed to her breast, white lips, dilated eyes filled with tears. . . . That's usually how I see her even in my sleep. . . . What did I push her away for? Even today when I recall it I feel as though my heart was being cut with a blunt knife.

'We were posted to our regiments at Biely Tserkov, in the Ukraine. I was given a lorry to drive. And on it I drove to the front. But I needn't tell you about the war; you saw it yourself and you know what it was like. I often had letters from my family, but I myself only sent postcards, and that rarely. I'd write that all was well, we were fighting but not too hard, and although we were retreating now, we'd soon gather our strength and then we'd give the Fritzes something to think about. And what else could you write? It was a gruelling time, not what you'd write home about. And I must admit I'm not the sort to sing a mournful tune; I couldn't stand the slobberers who wrote to their wives and sweethearts every day, whether there was any need for it or not, and smeared their snivels off the paper as they wrote. The sort who wrote that things were hard, and very difficult, they might be killed any moment. That sort of bitch in trousers would write down all his complaints, he'd work on their sympathy, he'd dribble away, and it would never occur to him that the unfortunate women and children in the rear were just as badly off as he was at the front. All the state was resting on their shoulders. And what shoulders our women and children did need to avoid being bent under that burden! But they didn't bend, they stood firm. But that drip, that wet little soul had to write his complaining letter, and it was like a stick between her feet to the woman working at home.

18

When she got that sort of letter she'd let her hands drop, she wouldn't feel at all like work. No! That's what you're a man for, that's what you're a soldier for: to endure everything, to bear everything, if necessary. But if you've got more a woman's spirit than a man's, then put on a skirt with flounces, so as to cover your fat arse more elegantly, so as to look like a woman at least from the back, and go and weed beetroots or milk the cows. But you're not needed at the front; there are enough there without you!

'However, it wasn't to be my lot to fight even a full year. Twice in that time I was wounded, but only lightly each time: once in the flesh of the arm, and once in the leg; the first time by a bullet from a plane, the second by a fragment of shell. The Germans made holes in the top and the sides of my lorry, but in the early days I was lucky, brother. I was lucky time after time; but my luck led me right into it.

'In May 1942 I was taken prisoner in a rather stupid way. The Germans were advancing fast at the time, and one of our 122-millimetre howitzer batteries ran out of ammunition; at the base my lorry was loaded with shells right to the top, and I myself worked so hard at the loading that my tunic stuck to my shoulders. We'd got to get a move on, for the battle was getting pretty close; on our left someone's tanks were blazing away, on the right was rifle fire, and ahead of us gunfire. Obviously something was cooking.

'The commander of our motor unit asks me: "Will you get through, Sokolov?" But really he didn't need to ask. My comrades might be dying out there, and was I going to stand around scratching myself? "What's the point of talking?" I answered. "I've got to get through, and that's all there is to it." "Well," he says, "off with you. Step on the gas!"

'And I did step on it. I'd never driven before as I did that day. I knew I wasn't carrying potatoes, I knew I ought to drive carefully with such a load. But who could stop to think of taking care when our boys out there were fighting with empty hands, and when the whole of the road was being shelled by the German artillery? I drove some four miles, and got close to a point where I had to turn off on to a by-road, in order to reach the ravine where the battery was in position. But

then – Holy Mother! – I see our infantry to right and left of
the road scattering over the open field, and mortars bursting
fast and furious behind them. Now what was I to do? Should
I turn back? I stepped on it even harder. Now I had less than
a mile to go to reach the battery; I'd already turned off the
main road. But I wasn't destined to get through to our men,
brother. A heavy artillery long-distance gun, it must have
been, put a shell down right by my lorry. I didn't hear the
explosion or anything, it was only as if something burst in my
head, and I remembered no more. How I came through that
time I don't understand, and how long I lay there, some eight
yards from the ditch, I've no idea. I came round, but I couldn't
get up; my head was twitching, shaking as if I was in a fever;
everything was dark before my eyes, there was a grating and
jarring feeling in my left shoulder, and the pain all over my
body was just as if I'd been beaten for two days on end with
whatever came to hand. I spent a long time wriggling on the
ground flat on my belly, but somehow at last I managed to get
up. Yet I still couldn't understand where I was or what had
happened to me. My memory had gone completely. But I
was afraid to lie down again. I was afraid I'd never get up
again, but just die where I lay. I stood there, swaying from
side to side, like a poplar in a storm.

'When I really came round, recovered my senses and looked
about me properly, my heart was pinched as if with a pair of
pliers: shells were scattered, the sort I'd been carrying, all
around me, not far away my lorry was lying upside down and
smashed to pieces, and the battle – the battle was already
going on behind me. How could that be?

'I don't mind confessing it, my legs gave way under me, and
I dropped as though pole-axed; for I realized that I was already
encircled, or, to put it better, I was a prisoner of the Fascists.
That's the sort of thing that happens in war. . . .

'Ah, brother, it's not pleasant to realize that whether you
like it or not you're a prisoner. If a man hasn't had that
experience personally it's hard to make him understand just
what it means to you.

'Well, as I lay there I heard tanks thundering along. Four
German medium tanks going at top speed went past me in the

20

direction I'd come from. How was I to survive that? Then motorized guns drove past, and a field kitchen; then infantry marching, not a lot, not more than a single full company. I watched and watched them out of the corner of my eye and then pressed my cheek close against the ground again, and closed my eyes. I felt sick just looking at them, and my heart was in my boots.

'When I thought everything had gone past I raised my head; and I saw six men armed with automatics striding along a hundred yards away. I saw them turn off the road and come straight at me. They came on silently. "Now," I thought, "here's death coming for me." I sat up, for I didn't want to die lying down; then I stood up. One of them halted a few paces away and slipped the automatic off his shoulder with a shrug. And, you know, man's a funny creature: no panic at all, nor any real fear did I feel at that moment. I only gazed at him, thinking: "He'll fire a short burst at me, but what will he aim at, my head or through my chest?" As if it made any difference which part of my body he drilled holes in!

'He was a young fellow, not at all bad-looking, swarthy; but his lips were as thin as threads and his eyes were narrowed. "He'll kill without thinking twice about it," I realized. And I was right! He threw up his automatic, and I gazed straight into his eyes, not saying a word. But another German, a corporal possibly, older than the first, elderly one might even say, shouted something, pushed him aside and came up to me, jabbering away in his own language. He bent my right arm at the elbow, feeling my muscle, it looked like. And then he said: "O-o-o!" and pointed to the road, in a westerly direction. Quick march, you working animal! Go and toil in our *Reich*! He proved a real husbandman, the son of a bitch!

'But the swarthy fellow took a good look at my boots – and I had on a good pair of boots – and pointed: "Take them off!" I sat down on the ground, took off my boots and gave them to him. He absolutely snatched them out of my hand. I unwound my leg-rags and held them out to him too, gazing up at him. But he bawled something, evidently swearing, and threw up his automatic again. The others laughed. And then they went off quietly. Except that the swarthy fellow looked back at me two or three times before he reached the road, his eyes flashing like a young wolf's; he looked furious; but why? You'd have thought I'd taken his boots, and not he mine.

'Well, brother, there was nothing else for it, so I went to the road, swore as only a lorry driver from Voroniezh can swear and set off westwards, to prison. My pace was pretty poor, it took me an hour to cover less than a mile. You try to go straight ahead, but you reel from side to side, you wander all over the road like a drunk. I hadn't gone far when I was overtaken by a column of our men from the same division as mine, all taken prisoner. They were being driven along by some ten to a dozen German soldiers with automatics. The German at the head of the column came up to me and, without saying a word, clubbed me on the head with the handle of his automatic. If I'd fallen he'd have stitched me to the ground with one burst; but our men caught me as I fell, pushed me into their middle and for half an hour they more or less carried me along. When I came to, one of them whispered: "For God's sake don't drop. Keep going with your last strength, or they'll kill you." I was at my last gasp, but I kept going.

'As soon as the sun set the Germans reinforced the convoy, brought up twenty more men armed with automatics on a lorry and drove us along faster. Those of our men who were badly wounded couldn't keep up with the rest, and they were shot on the spot. Two men tried to escape, but they didn't realize that in the open on a moonlight night you're almost as visible as in broad daylight; and of course they were both shot down. At midnight we arrived at some village half burnt to the ground. We were driven into a church with a shattered cupola for the night. There wasn't a blade of straw on the stone floor, and none of us had greatcoats, we were wearing only tunics and trousers, so we had nothing we could put down to lie on. Some of us weren't even wearing tunics, only cotton underwear. The majority of these were young junior officers; they'd taken off their tunics so that they couldn't be distinguished from privates. And the men from gun-teams also were without tunics. They'd been taken prisoner just as they were, stripped to the waist as they manned the guns.

'During the night rain fell so hard we were all soaked through.

22

The cupola had been carried away by a heavy-calibre shell or a bomb from a plane, and the rest of the roof was riddled with shells, so there wasn't a dry spot even by the altar. So all night we huddled together in that church like sheep in a dark cattle shed. In the middle of the night someone nudged me on the arm, and I heard him say: "Comrade, you're not wounded, are you?" I answered: "Why, what d'you want to know for, brother?" And he says: "I'm an army doctor, perhaps I can help you in some way?" I complained to him that my left shoulder grated and was swollen and hurt terribly. He said firmly: "Take off your tunic and vest." I took them off, and he began feeling my arm at the shoulder with his thin fingers, but so hard it made my head swim. I grated my teeth and said to him: "I can see you're not a proper doctor, you're a vet. What are you pressing on the painful spot like that for, you brute?" But he went on groping, and angrily answered: "Your job is to keep quiet! Thinking you'd like to have a nice little chat with me! Hold on, it'll hurt even more in a moment." And he gave my arm such a tug that crimson sparks flew from my eyes.

'When I got over it I asked: "What d'you think you're doing, you miserable Fascist? My arm's shattered to bits, and you go and tug it like that!" I heard him laugh quietly, and he said: 'I thought you'd land out at me with your right, but evidently you're a peaceable sort. Your arm isn't shattered, it was only dislocated, and now I've put it back. Well, how d'you feel now? Better?" I must admit that I did feel the pain going. I thanked him warmly, and he went on in the darkness, quietly whispering: "Any wounded around here?" That's what I call a real doctor. Even as a prisoner, even in the darkness, he went on with his great work.

'That was a restless night for us. They wouldn't allow us to go outside; the German in charge of the convoy had warned us about that when they drove us two by two into the church. As it happened, one fellow who'd got religion took it into his head to go outside to relieve himself. He tried hard to hold on, but couldn't, and he burst into tears. "I can't foul a holy temple," he said. "I'm a believer, I'm a Christian. What am I to do, brothers?" Well, you know what our soldiers are like.

23

Some of them laughed, others swore at him and others gave him all sorts of joking advice. He made us all laugh, but the business had a bad end: he started knocking on the door and asking to be let out. Well, he got what he asked for! The Fascist fired a long burst through the door, right across its width, and killed the devout man, and three others too. And a fourth who was badly wounded died during the night.

'We put all the dead in one spot, squatted down and were quiet. But we couldn't help thinking it wasn't a very cheerful beginning. However, after a while we started talking in undertones, whispering, trying to find out who was from where, what province and how he was captured. In the darkness comrades from a single platoon or acquaintances in one company had got separated, and they began calling quietly to one another. Right next to me I heard the following conversation. One man said, "When we fall in tomorrow, before we're driven on, if they call out the commissars, Communists, and Jews, don't you try to hide, troop commander. Nothing will come of it. D'you think that because you've got rid of your tunic you'll pass for a private? It won't wash! I don't intend to suffer through you. I'll be the first to point you out. I know you're a Communist and you tried hard to get me to join the party, so now you can answer for it." The voice was that of a man sitting next to me, on my left. From the other side of him a youthful voice answered: "I always suspected you were rotten, Krizhniov. Especially when you refused to join the party because you said you were illiterate. But I never thought you'd turn traitor. You passed right through the seven-year school, didn't you?" The other man slowly replied: "Well yes, I did, but what of it?" I heard nothing more for some time, but then the troop commander's voice came quietly: "Don't betray me, comrade Krizhniov." But the other man laughed softly. "The comrades," he said, "have been left behind on the other side of the front. I'm no comrade of yours, and don't plead with me, I'll point you out whatever happens. My own skin's more precious to me than yours."

'Neither of them said any more, but I turned cold at the thought of that swine. "No," I thought, "I shan't allow you to betray your commander, you son of a bitch. You'll never

24

leave this church alive; you'll be dragged out by your feet, like carrion." As soon as light began to come I saw an ugly-mug of a youngster lying next to me with his arms behind his head, and next to him a rather skinny, snub-nosed lad in only a vest was sitting with his arms round his knees, and looking very pale. "Well," I thought, "that boy won't be able to cope with such a fat gelding. I'll have to finish the blighter off."

'I touched the boy on his arm, and asked in a whisper: "Are you a troop commander?" He didn't answer, only nodded. "And he intends to betray you?" I pointed to the fellow lying down. He nodded again. "Well," I said, "you hold his legs so that he can't kick. But quick!" And I fell on the ugly-mug and gripped his throat with my fingers. He didn't have a chance to cry out. I lay down on top of him, gripping his throat, for several minutes, then I got up. The traitor was done for, his tongue would never wag.

'I felt so queer afterwards. I badly wanted to wash my hands, like as if I hadn't choked a man but a creeping reptile. It was the first time I'd ever killed anybody, and now it was one of our own men. But was he really one of us? He was a traitor, the worst of all. I got up and said to the troop commander: "Let's shift away from here, comrade; the church is large enough."

'As Krizhniov had said, next morning we were fallen in outside the church, and surrounded by men with automatics. Then three S.S. officers started picking out the men they thought dangerous. They asked which of us were Communists, who were commanders and who commissars. But we didn't appear to have any such among us. Nor did we have any swines prepared to betray them, for almost half our number were Communists, and of course we had commanders and commissars too. Out of two hundred men and more the Germans took away only four: one Jew and three Russian privates. The Russians had it because all three were swarthy and curly haired. The S.S. men went up to them and asked: "Yid?" The man said no, he was Russian; but the Germans wouldn't listen to him. "Step out of the rank!" And that was that.

'They shot those poor wretches, and the rest of us were driven on. The troop commander who'd helped me strangle the traitor kept beside me all the way to Poznan, and that first day, as we marched, he kept taking my hand and squeezing it. We got separated at Poznan, and it was like this:

'You see, brother, from the very first day I'd thought of escaping and getting back to our own people. But I wanted to be quite sure of success. As far as Poznan, where we were confined in a proper camp, not one suitable opportunity had come along. But in the Poznan camp a chance seemed to turn up: at the end of May we were sent out to a wood near the camp, to dig graves for our dead prisoners of war; at that time lots of the likes of us were dying of dysentery. As I dug the Poznan earth I kept looking about, and I noticed that two of our guards had sat down to have a smoke, while the third was dozing in the sun. I threw down my spade and slipped quietly behind a bush. . . . And then I started running, making straight for the east. . . .

'It must have been some time before our guards realized what had happened. But I just don't know where I got the strength to cover almost twenty-five miles on that first day, scraggy as I was from lack of food. However, nothing came of my dreams. I was caught three days later, though I was already a long way from the blasted camp. Dogs picked up my trail, and they found me in a field of standing oats.

'I was afraid of moving across open country in broad daylight, and it was at least a couple of miles to the nearest forest, so I hid among the oats for the day. I husked some grain in my palms, chewed a little and poured some more into my pocket as iron rations. But just then I heard dogs baying, and a motorbike engine. . . . My heart stopped beating, for the dogs were coming nearer and nearer. I lay down quite flat and covered my head with my arms, to make sure they didn't bite my face. They ran up to me, and in a moment they'd torn all my rags off me. I was left in my birthday suit. They rolled me over and over in the oats just as they liked, and in the end one bitch set her forepaws on my chest and aimed at my throat, but didn't actually bite me.

'Two Germans rode up on motorbikes. They began by

beating me to their hearts' content, and then set the dogs on me, and they tore shreds of skin and flesh off me. Then I was carried naked and all bloody back to the camp. I spent a month in the cells for trying to escape, but all the same I was alive. . . . I was still alive!

'It's not easy for me to recall, brother, and still harder to talk about all I had to suffer as a prisoner. When you think of the inhuman tortures we had to endure in Germany, when you remember all your friends and comrades who died, tortured to death in those camps, your heart doesn't stay in your chest but comes up into the throat, and you find it hard to breathe.

'The places I was shifted to during the two years I was a prisoner! In that time I travelled over a good half of Germany. I was in Saxony, working in a silicate works, and in the Ruhr I pushed coal trucks in the mines, and in Bavaria I developed a stoop working on the land, and then I spent some time in Thuringia; the devil knows whether there was any part of Germany I didn't have to work in. Everywhere in Germany nature is different, but everywhere the Germans beat the likes of us exactly the same, brother. And the goddamned reptiles and parasites beat us worse even than we treat our animals. They punched us with their fists, they kicked us, they beat us with rubber truncheons, and all kinds of iron, whatever came to hand, not to mention rifle butts and other bits of wood.

'They beat us because we were Russians, because we were still alive, and because we were working for them, the swines! And they beat us because we didn't look at them properly, we didn't walk properly, we didn't turn round properly. They beat us simply so as to beat us to death sooner or later, for us to sob out our last blood and die of the beatings. Evidently they hadn't got enough incinerators in Germany for all of us.

'And wherever we were, we always got the same food: 150 grammes of ersatz bread, half sawdust, and a thin brew made from mangolds. In some places we were given hot water, in others not. But why talk about it? Judge for yourself: before the war I weighed over 190 pounds, but by the first autumn I went no more than 130. I was nothing but skin and bones, and I didn't really have the strength even to carry my bones about.

27

But work you had to, and no complaining, and it was work that would have been too heavy for a carthorse.

'At the beginning of September we were transferred from a camp outside the town of Kustrin, a hundred and forty-two Soviet prisoners of war, to camp B 14, not far from Dresden. By that time there were some two thousand of us in the camp. We all worked at stone breaking; we dug out, broke and smashed the German stone by hand. The task set us was four cubic metres per day per soul; note: per a soul that was already only just holding on to the body by a single fine thread. And then we really went through it! In two months, out of the hundred and forty-two who'd been transferred together to the camp only fifty-seven were left. What d'you think of that, brother? Good going? We didn't have time to bury all our dead. And just about then the rumour spread through the camp that the Germans had taken Stalingrad and were pushing on towards Siberia. One misfortune after another! The news depressed us so much that we couldn't raise our eyes from the ground; we looked at it as if we were pleading to be taken into the foreign, German earth. But the camp guards got drunk every day, singing at the top of their voices and making merry over their victory.

'One evening after work we were returning to our barrack. Rain had been falling all day, you could have wrung the water out of our rags, we were shivering like dogs in the bitter wind, we couldn't keep our teeth from chattering. But we had nowhere to dry our clothes or get warm, and we were hungry not to death, but worse. But no food was ever dished out to us in the evening.

'I took my wet rags off, flung them on the bunk, and said: "They want four cubic metres from us, but one cubic metre would be sufficient for a grave for any one of us." I'd barely got the words out when some cur among us reported my bitter remark to the camp commandant.

'Our camp commandant, or *Lagerführer*, as they called him, was a German named Muller. He was of medium height, stout, with a fair complexion and quite bleached: his hair was white, and his eyebrows, and his eyelashes; even his eyes had a whitish tinge, and they goggled. He talked Russian as well as you or me, and even pronounced his o's very round, like a native of the Volga region. And as for swearing in Russian, he was an absolute master. Where had he learnt that art, the blackguard? He used to fall us in outside the barracks and walk along the line with his gang of S.S. men, with his right hand stretched out. He wore a leather glove, and in the glove was a piece of lead so as to protect his fingers. He'd walk along hitting every second man on the nose, making the blood flow. He called this a "prophylactic against the flu". And it happened every day. There were only four barracks in the camp, and one day he'd arrange a "prophylactic" for the first barrack, the next day for the second, and so on. He was very regular, the reptile, and he never had any days off. Only one thing the fool couldn't realize. Before he started to lash out with his hands he'd stand for ten minutes in front of our line swearing at us in order to work himself up! But somehow his curses missed the mark, and we even felt better for them; it was sort of as if the words were our own, native words, as if a breeze was blowing from our own country. . . . If he'd known we enjoyed his swearing he wouldn't have used Russian but his own language. However, one of my friends, a Moscow man, got really mad about it. "When he swears," he used to say, "I close my eyes and think I'm in Moscow, sitting in a pub, and I get such a hankering for beer that it makes my head swim."

'Well, this commandant, the day after I'd said my piece about the cubic metre, he sent for me. In the evening an interpreter came to the barrack, and with him two guards. "Which of you is Andrei Sokolov?" he asked. I answered. "March with us, *Herr Lagerführer* wants you." I knew what he wanted me for. To wipe me out. I sighed and said good-bye to my comrades – they all knew I was going to my death – and went out. As I walk across the camp yard I look up at the stars, say good-bye to them and think: "Well, so you've come to the end of your torture, Andrei Sokolov, number 331." Somehow I felt sorry for Irena and the children; but then the sorrow faded and I began to rally my spirits, so I could look at the pistol barrel without fear, as a soldier should; so that the enemy shouldn't see it was hard for me to part with life. . . .

'There were lights in the windows of the commandant's

house; it was as clean and neat as in one of our good clubs. The entire camp command was seated at the table; five men were sitting drinking schnapps and chewing ham. On the table was a large open bottle of schnapps, and bread, ham, pickled apples and open cans of preserves of various kinds. I took all that grub in with one glance, and – you won't believe it – the sight upset me so much I was nearly sick. There I was as hungry as a wolf, quite unused to human food, and all that good grub right under my nose. . . . Somehow I choked down my nausea, and forced myself to turn my eyes away from the table.

'Muller was sitting straight in front of me, half drunk, playing with his pistol, throwing it from hand to hand, while he stared at me without blinking, like a snake. I stood to attention, clicked my patched heels and reported in a loud voice: "Prisoner of war Andrei Sokolov present as you commanded, *Herr* commandant." And he asks: "Well, Russian Ivan, so you think four cubic metres is too heavy a task?" "Yes, *Herr* commandant," I said, "it's too much." "But one's enough for a grave for you?" "Yes, *Herr* commandant, it's quite enough and there'll be some left over."

'He stood up and said: "I'm going to do you a great honour; I'm going to shoot you myself this minute for what you've said. But it's not convenient in here, so we'll go out into the yard, you can be signed off there." "As you wish," I said. He stood for a moment, thinking, then he flung the pistol on the table and poured out a full glass of schnapps, picked up a small piece of bread, laid a tiny slice of ham on it and handed it all to me, saying: "Have a good drink, Russian Ivan, before you die. Drink to the victory of the German arms."

'I'd been about to take the glass and the food from him; but when I heard him say that I felt as if I'd been burnt. I thought to myself: "Am I, a Russian soldier, to drink to the victory of German arms? What difference does it make if I've got to die? You can go to hell with your vodka."

'So I put the glass down on the table, and the food too, and said: "Thank you for your hospitality, but I don't drink." He smiled: "So you don't want to drink to our victory? In that case, drink to your own perdition!" Well, what had I to lose? "I'll drink to my perdition and salvation from further torture," I said. And I picked up the glass and tossed off the liquor in two gulps. But I didn't touch the bread; I wiped my lips very politely with my palm, and said: "Thank you for your hospitality. I'm ready, *Herr* commandant; let's go and you can sign me off."

'But he stared at me hard, and said: "You ought to have a bite of something before you die." To which I answered: "I never eat after the first glass." He poured out a second and handed it to me. I drank the second glass too, but still I didn't touch the bread; I was growing bold, and I thought: "I'll have a good drink at least before I go out to part with life." The commandant raised his white eyebrows and asked: "Why aren't you eating, Russian Ivan? You needn't feel constrained." But I said: "Excuse me, *Herr* commandant, I'm not used to eating even after the second glass." He blew out his cheeks, snorted, then he roared with laughter and said something rapidly in German as he laughed, evidently translating my remarks to his pals. And they laughed too, wriggling in their chairs, eyeing me. And I noticed they were looking at me differently, sort of less sternly.

'The commandant poured out a third glass for me, and his hand shook with his laughter. I drank that glass down in sips, bit a small piece of bread, and put the rest back on the table. I wanted to show them, damn them, that although I was all but dropping with hunger I wasn't going to choke myself with their snack; I had my own, Russian, dignity and pride and they hadn't turned me into cattle, with all their trying.

'Then the commandant put on a serious look, adjusted the two iron crosses on his chest, came round the table without his pistol and said: "Well, Sokolov, you're a true Russian soldier. You're a brave soldier. I'm a soldier too, and I respect worthy opponents. So I shan't shoot you. And besides, our glorious troops have reached the Volga today and have completely occupied Stalingrad. That's great news for us, and so I magnanimously grant you your life. Go back to your barrack, and take this for your cheek." And he gave me a small loaf of bread and a piece of ham from the table.

31

'I pressed the bread against my chest with all my strength, took the ham in my left hand, and was so overwhelmed by this unexpected turn that I didn't even say "thank you". I did a right-about and went to the door, thinking as I went: "Now he'll let light into me between my shoulders, and I shan't get this grub back to the boys." But no: I got out. Death passed me by that time too, I only felt its cold breath on me.

'I walked out of the commandant's office on firm feet; but outside in the yard I went limp. I stumbled into the barrack and dropped unconscious on the concrete floor. Our men brought me round in the dark. "Tell us all about it." Well, I remembered what had happened in the commandant's office, and I told them. "How shall we share out the food?" my bunk neighbour asked, and his voice was shaking. "Equal shares for all," I answered. We waited for light to come. Then we cut up the bread with a damp thread. Every man got a tiny piece of bread the size of a matchbox, we took every crumb into account. But as for the ham: well, as you can guess, it only smeared our lips. All the same, we shared it out without missing anyone.

'Soon after that we were transferred, some three hundred of the strongest of us, to work draining marshes, and then to the Ruhr mines. There I remained until 1944. By that time our forces were twisting Germany's neck, and the Fascists stopped being snorty about prisoners of war. One day the entire day shift was assembled, and some visiting *Oberleutnant* said through an interpreter: "Anyone who worked as a motor driver in the army or before the war, one pace forward." Seven of us, all former drivers, stepped out. We were given worn overalls and sent under convoy to Potsdam. When we arrived we were all posted to different jobs. I was put to work in the Todt organization – this was a stupid administration the Germans had set up for road construction and defensive works.

'I drove an Opel-Admiral, for a German engineer with the rank of major. He was a fat Fascist, all right! Small, big in the belly, his length and breadth the same, and as broad in the beam as a matronly woman. Over his uniform collar he had three double chins, and three thick rolls of fat on the nape of his neck. I reckoned that there was not less than a hundredweight of pure fat on his carcass. As he walked he puffed away like a railway engine, and when he sat down to eat there was no stopping him! There were times when he spent the whole day chewing, and drinking cognac from a flask. Sometimes a scrap fell to me from his table: we'd halt on the road and he'd cut up sausage and cheese, he'd eat and drink, and if he was in a good humour he'd throw me a bit, as if I was a dog. He never handed it to me: oh, no, he regarded that as beneath his dignity. But no matter how things were, there was no comparison with the camp life, and little by little I began to look more like a human being; very slowly, I began to recover.

'For two weeks I drove my major from Potsdam to Berlin and back; but then he was sent up to the front-line zone to construct defensive works against our forces. And then I finally unlearnt how to sleep: all night long I'd lie awake wondering how I could escape to my own people, to my own country.

'We drove to the town of Plotsk. For the first time in two years I heard our artillery thundering away in the dawn. And can you imagine, brother, how my heart beat! Even when I used to go and meet Irena before we were married, even then it didn't beat so fast. The battle was being fought some twelve miles east of Plotsk. The Germans in the town were worked up and all on edge, and my fatty started drinking more and more. Each morning I'd drive him outside the town and he'd give instructions for building the defensive works; but at night he'd sit drinking, alone. He swelled all over, and great bags hung under his eyes.

' "Well," I thought, "there's no point in waiting any longer; this is my great chance. And I've got to do more than just escape on my own; I've got to take my fatty with me, he'll come in useful to our people."

'In some ruins I found a five-pound weight, wrapped it in rag so that there shouldn't be any blood if I had to use it, got hold of a length of telephone cable on the road, got everything I needed thoroughly ready and hid it all under the front seat. Two days before I said good-bye to the Germans I was driving back alone one evening from refuelling, and saw a German non-commissioned officer coming along as drunk as a lord, clinging to the wall with his hands. I stopped the car, dragged him into some ruins and shook him out of his uniform, took the cap off his head. And I stowed all this property also under the seat.

'On the morning of June 29th my major ordered me to drive him out of the town in the direction of Trosnitsa. He was organizing the construction of fortifications there. We set out. The major dozed peacefully on the back seat, but my heart was almost jumping out of my chest. I drove fast at first, but once out of the town I slowed down; then I stopped the car, climbed out and looked about me: a long way behind two lorries were moving slowly. I took out the weight, and opened the door wider. Fatty was lying against the back of the seat, snoring away as if he'd got his wife beside him. So I hit him with the weight on his left temple. And his head dropped. Just to make sure I gave him another blow, but not so as to kill him. I wanted to hand him over alive: he could tell our people a lot. I took his pistol from its holster, put it in my pocket, fixed up a fastening in the top of the back seat, put the telephone wire round the major's neck and tied it loosely to the fastening. That was so he shouldn't slip sideways and fall over as I drove fast. I hurriedly put on the German uniform and cap, and then drove at top speed in the direction where the earth was roaring, where the fighting was going on.

'I drove through the German main defences between two pillboxes. Men with automatics dashed out of a dug-out, so I deliberately slowed down so as to let them see a major was coming. But they raised a shout, and waved their arms about, evidently to tell me I couldn't go any farther in that direction. But I pretended not to understand; I stepped on the gas and drove on at a good fifty. By the time they'd realized something was wrong and started to fire at the car with machine-guns I was twisting and turning as neat as any hare between the craters of no-man's land.

'So the Germans were firing at me from behind, and then our own men went crazy, and welcomed me with fire from automatics. They holed the windscreen in four places and riddled the radiator with bullets. But I came to a wood by a lake, and as our men ran towards the car I drove into that wood, opened the door, fell to the ground and kissed it; and I hadn't any breath left. . . .

'A youngster with khaki epaulettes on his tunic, the like of which I'd never seen before, ran up to me and bared his teeth: "Aha, you bloody Fritz, so you've lost your way?" I tore off my German uniform, flung the cap under my feet, and said: "Hold hard, my dear son! How can I be a Fritz when I'm a born native of Voroniezh? I've been a prisoner of war, understand? But untie that hog sitting in the car, take his document case and lead me to your commander." I handed over the pistol and was passed along from hand to hand, and late in the afternoon I found myself in front of a colonel, the divisional commander. By that time they'd given me some food, I'd had a bath, they'd questioned me and put me in uniform: so I arrived at the colonel's dug-out in good order, clean in soul and body and in full uniform. The colonel rose from his table and came to meet me; in front of all the officers he embraced me and said: "Thank you, soldier, for the fine present you've brought us from the Germans. Your major and his document case are of more value to us than twenty 'reports'. I shall recommend the higher command to put your name forward for a government award." At his words, and his kindness, I got terribly worked up, my lips trembled and wouldn't obey me; all I could get out was: "I ask you, comrade colonel, to assign me to a rifle company."

'But the colonel laughed and clapped me on the back. "What sort of fighter would you make, when you can hardly stand on your feet? I'm sending you to hospital today. They'll get you well and feed you up, then you can go home to your family for a month on leave. And we'll see where to assign you to when you come back."

'And the colonel and all the officers in the dug-out shook my hand warmly when I left, and I came out quite overcome. For during the past two years I'd grown unused to being treated as a human being. And note, brother, that for a long time after, whenever I had to speak to an officer I involuntarily drew my head down out of habit, as if I was afraid they'd hit me. That's how we were educated in the Fascist camps. . . .

'As soon as I got into hospital I wrote a letter to Irena.

35

I told her briefly how I'd been a prisoner, and how I'd got away with a German major. For goodness sake, where had I picked up that childish trick of bragging! All the same, I couldn't keep it to myself, I told her the colonel had promised to recommend me for an award.

'For two weeks I only ate and slept. They fed me a little at a time, and often, for the doctor said if they'd let me eat as much as I wanted in one go I might have packed up altogether. I got my strength right back. But after two weeks I went right off my food again. I had no reply from home, and I must admit I was beginning to worry. Food isn't much good for the mind; I couldn't sleep, I started thinking all sorts of unpleasant thoughts. Then, during the third week, I had a letter from Voroniezh. But not from Irena; it was from a neighbour of mine, Ivan Timofeevich, a carpenter. God grant that others may never get a letter like it! He told me that as long ago as June 1942 the Germans had bombed the aeroplane works, and one heavy bomb had made a direct hit on my hut. Irena and my two daughters happened to be at home at the time. . . . He wrote that they didn't find a trace of them, and where the hut had been was a deep hole. . . . I didn't finish the letter right through that first time. My eyes went dark, my heart stopped beating and simply wouldn't pick up again. I lay down on my bed, and stayed there a little while, then I finished reading the letter. My neighbour wrote that at the time of the bombing Anatole was in the town. He returned to our place in the evening, looked at the hole and went back to the town that same night. Before he went he told my neighbour he was going to volunteer for the front. And that was all.

'When my heart recovered and the blood began to roar in my ears I remembered how hard Irena had found the parting from me at the station. So even then her woman's heart had told her we'd never see each other again in this world. But I'd pushed her away. . . . We'd had a family, our own house, all the things we'd got together over the years, and it had all vanished in a single moment. I was left alone. I thought: "Surely I didn't dream it all, this messy life of mine?" And yet, while I was a prisoner, almost every night I'd talked with Irena and the children, to myself, of course; I'd tried to give them courage, telling them: "I'll be coming back, my dears; don't grieve for me, I'm strong, I'll survive. And we'll all be together again." . . . Had I been talking for two years with the dead?'

He stopped for a moment, then said in a different tone, broken and softer:

'Let's have a smoke, brother, or I'll choke.'

We lit up. In the trees above the flood a woodpecker tapped noisily. The warm wind was still lazily stirring the dry catkins on the alders, the clouds were still floating in the blue as though under bellying white sails. But now, in that minute of mournful silence, I thought the boundless world, preparing for the great achievement of spring, the age-old confirmation of life, seemed different.

The silence was painful, and I asked:

'Then what happened?'

'What happened?' he answered reluctantly. 'I was given a month's furlough by the colonel, and in a week I was in Voroniezh. I walked out to the spot where at one time I'd been a family man. A deep crater flooded with rusty-looking water, and scrub up to the waist all around it. It was very still, the silence of a cemetery. Oh, it was hard for me, brother. I stood there, inwardly grieving, and then went back to the station. I couldn't stay there even an hour; I travelled back to the division that same day.

'But some three months later joy beamed on me like the sun from behind a cloud: Anatole turned up. He sent me a letter at the front, evidently from a different front. He'd learnt my address from our neighbour, Ivan Timofeevich. It appeared he'd been drafted into an artillery training school at first; they found his gift for mathematics useful there. In a year he'd passed out of the school with distinction, had gone to the front and now he wrote that he'd been raised to the rank of captain, was in command of a battery of "forty-fives", had been awarded six orders and medals. In a word, he'd outdone his father in every respect. And again I was terribly proud of him. Say what you like: my own son was a captain and a battery commander; that's not to be sneezed at! And with all those orders too! What did it matter that his father

37

was carrying shells and other military supplies on his Stude-baker? His father had had his day; but for the son, the captain, the future held out everything.

'And I began to have an old man's dreams at night: when the war was over I'd marry off my son and would go to live with the young couple, I'd work as a carpenter and dandle my grandchildren. In a word, just an old man's fantasies. But then it was all knocked on the head. During the winter we advanced without stopping, and so we didn't have much time to write to each other. But towards the end of the war, when we were close to Berlin, one morning I sent Anatole a little note, and I got his reply the very next day. And then I realized that I and my son had reached the German capital by different routes, but that now we were quite close to each other. I couldn't wait, but I just had to: I lived for the day when we'd meet again. Well, we met. . . . Right on the ninth of May, on the morning of the Day of Victory, my Anatole was killed by a German sniper.

'That afternoon I was sent for by my company commander. I saw he had some strange lieutenant-colonel of artillery sitting with him. As I entered the room the officer stood up as if I were his senior in rank. My company commander said: "He's come to see you, Sokolov," and turned away to look out of the window. I felt as though I'd had an electric shock, for I sensed that some misfortune had happened. The lieutenant-colonel came up to me and said quietly: "Be brave, father! Your son, Captain Sokolov, was killed today as he was standing by his battery. Come with me."

'I staggered, but I kept my feet. Now I remember as if it was a dream how I rode with the lieutenant-colonel in a large car, how we made our way through streets littered with rubble; I have a vague memory of soldiers drawn up, and a grave lined with red bunting. But I saw Anatole just as I see you now, brother. I went up to the grave. My son was lying in it, yet it was not my son. I'd always seen my son as a smiling, narrow-shouldered little boy with his adam's apple showing strongly on his thin neck. But in that grave a young, broad-shouldered, handsome man was lying, with eyes half closed as though he was gazing right past me into some far distance unknown to me.

38

Only in the corners of the mouth my former son's little smile had remained fixed for ever. That was all I had known before. . . . I kissed him and stepped back. The lieutenant-colonel made a speech, my Anatole's comrades and friends wiped away their tears; but it seemed as if my unwept tears had dried up inside my heart. Perhaps that's why it aches so much?

'I buried my last joy and hope in alien German earth. The battery fired a salute to my son, accompanying its commander on his long journey, and then it was as if something snapped inside me. . . . As I went back to my company I was almost beside myself. But not long after, I was demobilized. Where was I to go? Certainly not to Voroniezh! Not for anything! I remembered I had a friend living in Uriupinsk; he'd been demobilized the previous winter after being wounded. At one time he'd invited me to go and stay with him. I remembered him, and went to Uriupinsk.

'My friend and his wife had no children; they had their own small house on the outskirts of the town. Although he was a war-wounded and had a pension, he worked as a driver for a transport company, and I got a job there too. I settled in with my friends, they gave me a home. We transported all sorts of goods over the district, and in the autumn we were turned on to carting grain. It was then I made the acquaintance of my new son, the one playing in the sand over there.

'When we used to arrive back in the town after a trip, of course our first idea was to drop into a teashop and have a bite to eat, and of course to get a drink of something stronger, just to take off our tiredness. I must mention that I'd already got thoroughly in the grip of that injurious habit. One day I saw that little boy hanging around the teashop; and he was there next day too. Such a small little ragamuffin he was, his face smothered with watermelon juice, and covered with dust; he was as filthy as earth, his hair all over the place. But his little eyes were like stars at night after rain. And I took such a fancy to him that, strange to say, I even started keeping my eyes open for him, hurrying back from a trip in order to see him the sooner. He used to get his food by hanging around the teashop and eating whatever anyone chose to give him.

'On the fourth day, with my lorry loaded with grain straight from the Soviet farm I turned off my road to go to the teashop. My little lad was sitting on the verandah, kicking his heels and, by the look of him, hungry. I put my head out of the window and shouted to him: "Hey, Vaniusha, get into the lorry with me; I'll drive and unload at the elevator, and then we'll come back here and have some dinner." At my shout he started, jumped down off the verandah, scrambled on to the lorry step and said quite quietly: "But how did you know my name's Vania, uncle?" And he opened his eyes wide as he waited for my answer. Well, I just told him I'd knocked about the world a bit and knew everything.

'He came round to the near side, I opened the door, seated him beside me and drove off. He was a bright little kid; but suddenly he went quiet for some reason, thinking over something. Then he kept glancing up at me from under his long curly lashes and sighing. Such a tiny little mite, and he'd already learnt to sigh! That wasn't right for a kid! I asked him: "And where's your daddy, Vania?" He whispers: "He died at the front." "And your mummy?" "She was killed by a bomb in the train we were in." "But where had you come from?" "I don't know, I don't remember." "And you haven't any family or relations left?" "No one." "But where d'you sleep at nights?" "Wherever I can."

'Burning tears welled up inside me, and I at once decided: "I can't allow him and me to go our separate ways and be lost to each other. I'll take him as my child." And at once I felt brighter and light of heart. I bent over him and quietly asked: "Vaniusha, do you know who I am?" He just asked, and sighed as he asked: "Who are you then?" And I said to him just as quietly: "I'm your daddy."

'My God, the thing that happened then! He flung himself round my neck and kissed me on the cheeks, on the lips, on the forehead and cried out so thin but loud, like a waxwing, that in the cab it was deafening: "My darling daddy! I knew it! I knew you'd find me. All the same, you'd find me. I waited so long for you to find me." He huddled against me and his body was trembling all over, like grass under the wind. But my eyes were moist, and I was trembling too, and my hands were shaking. . . . How I managed to keep hold of the wheel I don't know. It was a miracle. But as it was I ran into the ditch and stalled the engine. While I had that mist in my eyes I was afraid to drive on, for fear I ran into someone. We stopped for at least five minutes, and my little son was still huddling against me with all his puny strength, silent, trembling. I embraced him with my right arm, gently squeezed him against myself, and with my left hand I turned the lorry round and drove to my room. Why worry about the elevator? I wasn't interested in the elevator at that moment.

'I left the lorry by the gate, picked up my new little son in my arms and carried him into the house. But just as he'd wound his little arms round my neck, so now he clung on to me, pressing his cheek against my unshaven cheek, sticking like a burr. And so I carried him in. My friend and his wife happened to be at home. I went in, winked at them with both eyes and said boldly: "Look! I've found my Vaniusha. Take us in, good folk." They realized, both my childless friends at once realized what I was up to, and they went bustling and hurrying around. But I couldn't get my son away from clinging round my neck. Yet somehow I managed it at last. I washed his hands with soap and seated him at the table. My friend's wife poured him out a plate of cabbage soup, and when she saw how greedily he ate it her eyes filled with tears. She stood by the stove, crying into her apron. My Vaniusha saw she was crying, and ran to her, tugged at her skirt and said: "What are you crying for, auntie? Daddy found me outside the teashop, everybody ought to be glad, but you're crying." But that opened her flood-gates even wider. She was completely bowled over.

'After dinner I took him to the barber to get his hair cut, and when we got back home I bathed him myself in a flour trough, and wrapped him in a clean sheet. He put his arms round me and fell asleep in my arms. I laid him carefully on the bed, and drove off to the elevator. After unloading the grain I drove the lorry back to the car park and went running round the shops. I bought him cloth trousers, a shirt, sandals and a cap made of bast. Of course, everything turned out to be the wrong size, and the quality was hopeless. My landlady even went for me about the trousers. "You've gone clean out of your mind," she said, "to dress a child in cloth trousers in this hot weather." And in a moment she had her sewing machine out on the table, rummaged in their linen chest, and an hour later she had satin knickers run up for my Vaniusha, as well as a white shirt with short sleeves. I lay down to sleep at his side, and slept peacefully for the first time in many months. All the same, I got up four times during the night. I'd wake up and find him nestling under my arm like a sparrow under the eaves, snoring quietly, and I felt so happy inside, I just can't say how happy. I tried not to turn over so as to avoid disturbing him, but in the end I grew impatient and got up very quietly, struck a match and rejoiced at the sight of him.

'I woke up again before daylight came, wondering why I felt stifled. But that little son of mine had slipped out of the sheet and was lying right across me; he'd flung himself out and was pressing on my throat with one little foot. It's a restless business sleeping with him even now; but I've got used to it, I'd be worried without him. You gaze at him sleeping at night, you sniff at his rumpled hair, and your heart stops; it grows softer. And mine had gone quite stony with sorrow.

'At first I used to take him with me on my trips; but then I realized that it wasn't really good for him. What do I need myself? A crust of bread and some onion with salt, and a soldier's filled for a whole day. But he was a different kettle of fish: I'd got to get milk for him, and cook an egg; he simply couldn't go without hot food. But my work wouldn't wait. So I plucked up courage and left him in the care of my landlady; and he would cry all day, and then in the evening steal off to the elevator to meet me. He used to wait there till late at night.

'I had a hard time of it with him at first. Once we went to bed while it was still light; I'd had a hard day and was very tired, and as for him – usually he twittered away like a little sparrow, but for some reason that evening he was very quiet. I ask him: "What are you thinking about, little son?" So then he asked me, gazing up at the ceiling: "Daddy, what did you do with your leather jacket?" But I'd never had a leather jacket in my life. So I had to wriggle out of it. "I left it behind in Voroniezh," I told him. "But why were you so long looking for me?" I told him: "My son, I looked for you in Germany, and in Poland, and I walked and rode all through Belorussia, and then you turned up in Uriupinsk." "But is Uriupinsk nearer to Germany? And was it far from our home to Poland?" That's how we talked together before going to sleep.

'But d'you think he'd asked about that leather jacket just out of curiosity, brother? No, it wasn't so simple as that. It seems his real father had worn a leather jacket at some time or other, and he remembered it. For a child's memory is like summer lightning: it flashes, lights up everything for a moment and then fades. And my son's memory is like summer lightning: it works in flashes.

'Maybe he and I would have gone on living another year or more in Uriupinsk; but in the November I ran into trouble. I was driving through the mud, and in a village my lorry skidded and I knocked over a cow. Well, you know how it is at such times: the women started bawling, the people came running and the car inspector was on to me like a shot. He took my driving licence away, though I pleaded with him to be merciful. The cow got up, tucked in its tail and went galloping down the alleys; but I'd lost my licence. During the winter I worked as a carpenter, and then I wrote to a friend, a comrade from my regiment – he works as a lorry driver in your province, in Kashara district – and he invited me to join him. He wrote that I could work for six months in the carpenter's shop, and then I could get a fresh licence in his province. And so I and my little son are on our way to Kashara by forced marches.

'But, all the same, I ought to tell you that even if I hadn't run into that cow I'd have left Uriupinsk. I'm too eaten up with longing to sit in one place for long. But when my Vaniusha's grown a bit more and I have to send him to school, then, maybe, I'll quieten down and stay in one spot. But for the time being I go walking with him all over our Russian earth.'

'It must be hard going for him,' I remarked.

'But he doesn't travel much on his own feet, most of the time he rides on my back. I sit him on my shoulders and carry him. But if he wants to stretch his legs he slips down and runs along at the side of the road, kicking up his heels like a young kid. It would be nothing, brother, somehow we'd manage

43

together. But, you know, my heart's wearing a bit, the pistons are slapping. . . . Sometimes it gives me such a turn with its thumping that the world goes dark before my eyes. I'm afraid one of these days I'll die in my sleep and give my little son a fright. And there's one other misfortune: almost every night I see my dear dead ones in my sleep. Usually it's just as though I'm behind barbed wire, and they're free, on the other side of the wire. . . . I talk with them about everything, with Irena and with the children. But as soon as I try to pull the wire down with my hands, they go away as though they were melting out of my sight. . . . And it's a strange thing: during the day I always keep a tight grip on myself, you can't squeeze a groan or a sigh out of me. But in the night I wake up and my pillow is all wet with tears. . . .'

I caught the sound of my comrade's voice through the alder woods, and the splash of oars in the water.

The man, who had grown so close to me though he was a stranger, got up and held out his large hand, as hard as wood:

'Good-bye, brother; good luck!'

'And I hope you get safely to Kashara.'

'Thank you. Come on, son, let's go to the boat.'

The boy ran up to his father, ranged himself at his side and, holding on to the edge of the man's padded coat, trotted along beside him as he strode away.

Two orphaned human beings, two little grains of sand flung into strange lands by a war hurricane of unprecedented strength. What awaits them in the future? One would like to think that this Russian, a man of indomitable resolution, will come through, and that the boy will grow up by his fatherly shoulder, and, when he is full grown, will be able to endure all things, overcome all things on his way, if his native land calls him to its service.

As I watched them go I had a feeling of profound sorrow. Maybe everything would have gone off well at our parting; but after going a few steps Vaniusha, tripping over his little feet, turned round to me and waved his rosy fist. And suddenly I felt as though a soft but taloned paw had clutched at my heart; and I turned away hurriedly. No, not only in sleep do tears come to elderly men gone grey during the years of war.

They come in broad daylight too. The main thing is to know just when to turn away. And the most important thing of all is not to wound the heart of a child, to make sure he doesn't see the burning but scanty masculine tears running down your cheek.

1956

STORIES: 1923–1927

The Test

*An Incident in the Life of a certain County
in Dvinsk Province*

'If I remember aright, comrade Tiutikov, you used to be
a member of the party?' the secretary of the Young Communists' County Committee said to the man sitting opposite him.
The man was wearing a fashionable loose-fitting overcoat; his
self-satisfied eyes were sunk in rolls of fat.

Tiutikov fidgeted uneasily on the worn chintz seat of his chair
and muttered uncertainly:

'Hm, yes . . . you see I . . . er . . . went in for a little trading,
and, you see . . . in a word, at my own request I was expelled
from the party.'

'Well, all I wanted to say was this: the secretary of the
party's district branch, Pokusayev, is to travel to the district
centre on the same cart as you. He's being sent to the Agri-
cultural Exhibition. I personally know him only very slightly,
and I'd like to ask you as a former party member to do something for us. You'll be riding together, so I suggest you pretend
to be some N.E.P. man (you look ideal for the part), and try
to win his confidence, little by little. Find out his views on
the Young Communist movement, and what his Communist convictions are. Try to get him talking frankly, and when
you get to the district centre write and let me know the result.'

'A sort of minor political examination,' Tiutikov said, smugly
nodding his head on its fat neck, and smiling.

'Just write that you've arrived safely,' the secretary called
from the verandah, after seeing Tiutikov to the door.

Evening. Travelling by road . . . through the mud. . . .
Dangling his long legs over the side, Pokusayev dozed off to

49

the measured creaking of the cart, while shadows wandered over his bony freckled face. Tiutikov sat contemplating that face for some time; then he took some bread, sausage and cucumber out of his case and began chewing noisily. Pokusayev was disturbed from his doze. He seated himself at Tiutikov's side and, thoughtfully gazing at the nag's hindquarters with their patches of hairless skin, recalled with a sigh that he had forgotten to bring any food with him for the journey.

'Going to the exhibition?' Tiutikov asked as he gulped down another mouthful.

'Yes.'

'Hm, that's a stupid business. The people haven't got enough to eat, but they go and think up an exhibition.'

'It'll bring a lot of benefit to the peasants,' Pokusayev answered reluctantly.

'That sounds stupid to me.'

Pokusayev swung one leg, and made no comment.

'They're building things that aren't needed, they're superfluous. Take those Young Communists, for instance. They're simply hooligans. They ought to have been closed down long ago.'

'Don't let your tongue wag. That sort of talk will get you into trouble.'

'I'm not in the government, otherwise I'd damn well put a stop to them. I'd write out some good prescriptions for those Young Communist rascals. The villains, the atheists!'

By now the lights of the district centre were twinkling in the distance; but Tiutikov, choking himself with sausage, went on cursing and threatening the atheistic Young Communists.

'Now they've thought up the idea of building an air fleet. The wretches deserve a good flogging . . .' he rattled away hoarsely, taking sidelong glances through his pince-nez at Pokusayev. 'And all the bosses . . .'

But he was not destined to finish that remark. Pokusayev half rose and, without saying a word, pushed his skinny belly clumsily into his neighbour's back.

Two human bodies flew off the cart and into the squelching mud. The horse came to a halt. Tiutikov, scared out of his wits, tried to get up; but the infuriated secretary, breathing heavily, straddled his long legs and sent Tiutikov down again on his back. Grunting and groaning came from the shapeless heap of bodies.

'The district . . . secretary . . . asked me . . . as a sort of joke,' a stifled voice muttered; but the only answer was a furious bellowing and noises like someone beating a sack of oats. . . .

'Unquestionably a very reliable youngster,' Tiutikov wrote from the district centre. 'But . . .' He glanced at his muddy overcoat, fingered his grazed knee and whispered indistinctly with his swollen lips. 'But . . .'

He looked sadly at the broken glass of his pince-nez, scratched the blue bridge of his nose with his pen handle and, with a hopeless gesture, ended his letter:

'None the less, I arrived safely.'

1923

The Three

Dedicated to the Pokrovsky Workers' Faculty

At first there were two of them. One was large and made of bone; it had an aristocratically querulous face, and gave off the hardly perceptible scent of eau de cologne. The other was small, made of wood and trimmed with red cloth.

The third, blue and made of metal, was brought in only the other day. After his morning clean-up the yardman thought he would like a smoke, and he pulled it out of his pocket together with his packet of home-grown tobacco. He turned it over and over contemptuously in his horny, tobacco-stained fingers and dropped it on the window-sill, remarking:

'Sew it on my pants, Anna; I've lost a button off them.'

The blue button clattered boldly with its little metallic legs: 'Hello, comrades . . .'

The red button smiled dejectedly, and the bone one pulled a contemptuous face.

As they lay together on the damp window-sill of the yard-man's lodge they gradually fell into conversation.

'Really, gentlemen, I don't understand how it is I'm still alive,' the bone button began, talking with an aristocratic lisp. 'The smell of leg-rags, that specifically "peasant smell", is a nightmare. Two months ago I was living on a magnificent overcoat, third from the top. My owner was a big manufacturer in the old days, but now he's got himself fixed up in some trust. He always did have money to burn. Often, when he took clean, rustling notes out of his notecase he'd whisper: "I'll finish up in the G.P.U. . . . They're bound to get me." And his fingers would tremble. Sometimes of an evening we'd drive with a dashing coachman to a certain artiste (he wasted a lot of money on her). Then we'd go for a long drive through the streets. Once they got out not far from a casino. "Come along," she

52

whispered and, getting hold of me, she drew him towards the door. "You're driving me into crime," he shouted, tearing himself away. I was left in her hand. She spat after him and flung me down on the pavement. After many wanderings I found myself here. But say what you like, the prospect of adorning some stinking peasant's trousers doesn't attract me at all, and I'm seriously thinking of committing suicide.' The bone button squeezed out a muddy tear and said no more.

'Yes, love is a great thing,' remarked the red button. 'At one time I shone on the cap of a Red Commissar. I took part in the fight against Wrangel, and against Makhno. The bullets whistled past me. At Perekop a cossack sabre all but sliced me in two. Those days passed like a glorious dream. Then a lull came. . . . My Red Commissar began to perspire under his cloth Budionny cap, as he studied mathematics and other learned subjects. But he happened to make the acquaintance of a young lady typist, and everything went to pot. The threads holding me on grew weak, and the Red Commissar went yellow in the face; and when he saw me hanging by a thread and all but falling off he sighed mournfully and muttered something in defence of Trotsky.'

'Bourgeois ideology!' the metal button smiled sarcastically. 'The way I got here was much simpler. I was on the trousers of a Young Communist studying in a Workers' Faculty.'

The bone button pulled down the corners of its lips contemptuously; the red button turned pink with embarrassment.

'My owner,' the metal button continued, 'was shock-headed, with beetling brow and merry eyes. He studied hard. When he wasn't studying he worked like a coolie at the railway station and sang "The Young Guard" all day. Cutting down his spending to the bare necessities, he bought himself a new pair of trousers, and me with them. I can't say I belonged to him alone. On the contrary, another five peasant lads just as fine as he was had my services too. They used to put on the trousers in turn, and they smelt, young and strong as they were, not of eau de cologne but of youth and strength. The shock-headed one was always reading. He often made speeches in the district committee. When he couldn't think of a suitable expression he was fond of pulling up his trousers. Though often he had to pull them up because he'd got nothing in his belly. I was soaked through and through with the smell of Communism and, believe me, I felt fine and dandy. One day the boys came home gloomy and sorrowful. They'd got to buy a book, *Historical Materialism*, and to subscribe to the paper *Youthful Truth*, and they hadn't any money. They sat silent, thinking, for a couple of hours. Then the shock-headed one gave me an affectionate tug with his fingers and said resolutely: "Either we finish our studies at the Workers' Faculty, or we go about in new trousers. So let's go and flog them in the Sukharevka market, boys." The whole lot of them pulled his trousers off him, thoroughly enjoying the joke. But in the confusion they pulled me off too. Half an hour later they were all lying on the floor reading *Historical Materialism*, while I was lying under a bed and thinking: "If sooner or later a staunch fighting Communist comes of that shock-headed lad it'll be partly due to me. . . ."

'Yes, of course . . .' the bone button lisped.

But the metal button spat on the floor with the utmost contempt and turned its back on its neighbours.

1923

Iliusha

The start of it all was a bear hunt.

Auntie Daria was chopping up firewood in the forest, in a dense thicket, and all but fell into a bear's den. Old Daria's quick-witted; she left her little son on guard not far from the lair, and ran to the village as fast as her legs would carry her. She rushed straight into Trofim Nikitich's hut.

'Is the master at home?'

'Yes.'

'I've come across a bear's den. . . . Kill it and give me a share.'

Trofim Nikitich looked her up and down, then down and up, and said suspiciously:

'If you're not lying, lead us to it and you'll have your share.'

So they made ready and went. Daria hobbled along in front, with Trofim Nikitich and his son behind. They had bad luck: they startled a big-bellied she-bear out of her lair, and fired at her almost point blank; but either they took disgracefully bad aim or for some other reason the bear escaped. Trofim Nikitich examined his ancient rifle as though it were to blame, swore long and juicily, looking sidelong at the grinning Ilia, and said at last:

'We simply can't let the animal get away. We'll have to spend the night in the forest.'

Next morning they saw that the bear had made off eastwards through the shaggy young pine trees, towards the Glinish-chevsky forest. Her track was clearly marked on the virgin snow; following the wandering trail, Trofim and his son roamed around for two days. They had to face cold and hunger – they finished their stock of food on the second day – and only after the third day did they catch the she-bear napping, in a little glade, under a solitary mournful birch. And then Trofim Nikitich said for the first time, as he watched his son shifting the six-hundred-pound carcass:

'But you've got some strength, my boy! Time we married you off. I'm growing old and feeble, I can't track down an animal and I miss my aim, my eyes water too much. Look, the bear's got children, offspring in her belly. . . . And that's what man's for, too.'

Ilia thrust the blood-stained knife into the snow, swept his sweaty hair off his forehead and thought: 'Now it's starting.'

And so it had. Not a day passed without his mother and father putting him more and more persistently into circulation: 'Get married; do get married! It's time you did, your mother's grown too old for work, we need a young mistress in the house to help the old woman.' And all that sort of talk.

Ilia sat on the stove, listening, breathing heavily, but saying nothing; until at last he grew thoroughly fed up with their nagging. Behind their backs he slipped a saw into a sack, picked up an axe and other carpentry tools, and began preparing for a journey. But the journey was not to be haphazard; he planned to go to the capital, to his uncle Yefim, who worked for the salesmen in the Moscow Village Industry stores.

His mother never stopped her nagging:

'I've found a bride for you, Ilia my dear. She's fine and just right for you, she's a pure juicy apple. She can work in the fields and keep guests amused with pleasant talk. We must get you engaged, or someone else will steal her from you.'

Their talking made the lad feel quite ill; he went into a decline. He hated the idea of getting married; to tell the truth he hadn't seen any girl he liked, none of those in any of the surrounding villages suited him. And when he learnt that his parents were proposing the shopkeeper's daughter as his bride his hair stood on end.

Next morning, after eating a breakfast of sorts, he said good-bye to his parents and went off to the station as fast as his legs could carry him. His mother cried at the parting; but his father, knitting his bushy brows, said angrily and bitterly:

'Since you want to go wandering, Ilia, off with you! But

don't come back home. I see you've been infected with Young Communism; you're always hanging about with them, the heathens. Well, now you can make your own life as best you can; I shan't try to lay down the law to you any more.'

He slammed the door behind his son, and gazed through the window as Ilia strode off down the street, erect and broad-shouldered. As the old man listened to his wife's bitter sobbing he frowned and gave a deep sigh.

2

There's no comparing Moscow with Kostroma. At first Ilia was terrified by every car horn; he trembled as he looked at the trams thundering by. But then he grew used to the traffic. His uncle Yefim got him a job as a carpenter. One night he left work rather late to go home under the silent rows of yellow-eyed street lamps. To shorten his road he turned into a quiet, winding alley. As he passed one of the gateways he heard a stifled cry, stamping feet and the sound of a slap on a face. He quickened his steps, and looked into the darkness of the gateway: by a damp vaulted wall a drunken pig, in an overcoat with an Astrakhan collar, was pawing some woman, panting and muttering thickly:

'Now. . . . Let me, my dear. . . . At our age it's so simple. Just a moment's happiness.'

Beyond the Astrakhan collar Ilia saw a crimson kerchief and a girl's eyes, filled with tears, terror and revulsion.

He strode up to the drunk, seized the Astrakhan collar and banged the flabby body against the wall. The man groaned, fixed his senseless ox-eyes on Ilia and, seeing the lad's stern eyes glaring at him, turned away and ran off down the alley, looking round and stumbling as he went.

The girl in the crimson kerchief and a shabby leather jacket clung tightly to Ilia's sleeve:

'Thank you, comrade. Very many thanks indeed.'

'What was he pawing at you for?' Ilia asked, shifting from foot to foot in his embarrassment.

'He's some drunken beast who tried to hitch himself on to me. I'd never seen him before. . . .'

57

She slipped a piece of paper with her address on it into Ilia's hand, and said again and again as they walked along to Zubovsky Square:

'Come and see me any time you're free, comrade. I'll be glad. . . .'

3

Ilia went along to see her on the following Saturday. He climbed up to the sixth floor, and read the name on the weather-beaten door: "Anna Bodrukhina." He stopped, felt in the darkness for the door handle and knocked very softly. She herself opened the door, and stood short-sightedly screwing up her eyes. Then she recognized him, and broke into a smile:

'Come in, please do.'

Mastering his shyness, Ilia sat down on the very edge of a chair and looked around the room. He answered her questions with spasmodic, broken sentences.

'From Kostroma . . . a carpenter. I've come to Moscow to work. . . . I'm twenty-one.'

But when he blurted out that he had run away from home to avoid being married off to a pious wife Anna laughed her head off, and pleaded insistently:

'Tell me about it again; do tell me.'

As he looked at her flushed face wrinkled with laughter, he, too, had to laugh. Awkwardly gesticulating, he told her a long story of all that had happened to him; and they both interlarded the story with their laughter, youthful and spring-like. He began visiting her frequently. The small room with its faded wallpaper and a portrait of Lenin on the wall attracted him strongly. After his day's work he found it pleasant to go and sit with Anna, to listen to her naïve stories of Lenin and to look into her eyes; they were grey with a tinge of bright sky-blue.

The streets of Moscow blossomed with the mud of spring. One day he went along to see her straight from work, set his tools down by the door, took hold of the handle and was startled to see a note in her familiar sloping handwriting: 'Gone away for a month, ordered to Ivanovo-Voznesensk'.

He walked down the stairs, gazing emptily into the darkness. His heart felt empty, too. He counted how many days would have to pass before she returned, And the nearer the longed-for day came, the greater grew his impatience.

On that Friday he did not go to work, but, not bothering about breakfast, first thing in the morning he turned into the familiar little street; it was flooded with the juicy scent of flowering poplars. His eyes picked out and watched every red kerchief that came along. Late in the afternoon he saw her coming out of the street and, unable to control his feelings, ran to meet her.

4

Now he was again spending his evenings with her, either in her room or at the Young Communists' club. She taught him to read, and then to write. In his fingers the penholder shook like an aspen leaf, blots fell on the paper; for her crimson kerchief was bent close to his face, and his head felt as though a smith were beating a measured and burning tattoo on his temples.

The pen shook in his fingers; broad-shouldered, crooked letters, rather like Ilia himself, found their way on to the paper. But his eyes were misted, misted.

A month or so later Ilia handed the secretary of the party branch on the construction site an application for membership of the Young Communist League. It wasn't any old application, but written with his own hand, in sloping and squiggly lines, which looked like foaming plane shavings.

One evening a week later Anna met him at the foot of the silent six-story building, greeting him with a ringing, joyous shout:

'Welcome to comrade Ilia, the Young Communist.'

5

'Now Ilia, it's two o'clock already. Time you went home.'

'Wait a bit. Or are you afraid you won't have time enough for a proper sleep?'

'For two nights running I haven't had sufficient sleep. Do go, Ilia.'

'It's very muddy in the street. My landlady will start moaning: "Out all night, and I've got to open and close the door for all of you quite unnecessarily." '

'Then you should go home earlier, not sit on and on here till midnight.'

'Perhaps I could . . . perhaps you could find a corner for me somewhere . . . to spend the night?'

She rose from the table and turned with her back to the light. Her forehead was furrowed with a slanting frown like a trench.

'Now listen, Ilia . . . if you're trying to hitch on to me, cast off again. I've noticed recently what you're after. I ought to tell you I'm married. My husband has been in Ivanovo-Voznesensk for four months, and I'll be going to see him in a few days' time.'

Ilia's lips felt as though they had been smeared with ashes.

'You're . . . married?'

'Yes. I'm living with a Young Communist. I'm sorry I didn't tell you before.'

He didn't go to work for two weeks. He lay on his bed, his face swollen and ashen. Then he dragged himself to his feet, touched his rusty saw with his finger and forced a strained wry smile.

When he turned up the other lads in the party branch questioned him:

'What bug has bitten you? Why, Ilia, you look like a walking corpse. What's turned you so yellow?'

In the club passageway he ran into the branch secretary:

'Is that you, Ilia?'

'Yes.'

'Where've you got to of late?'

'I was ill. . . . My head ached or something.'

'Listen: we've been allocated a place at a course in agronomy. Would you take it?'

'But I can only just read and write. . . . Otherwise I would.'

'Don't worry. They'll be holding preparatory classes, and I expect they'll teach you.'

60

One evening a week later Ilia was going straight from work to attend the course when he heard someone call behind him: 'Ilia!'

He looked back; Anna was running after him, smiling as she came. She shook his hand vigorously.

'Well, how are you getting on? I hear you're studying.'

'I'm managing, little by little; and yes, I'm studying. Thank you for teaching me my letters.'

They walked along side by side. But his head no longer swam from the proximity of her crimson kerchief. As they separated she asked, smiling and looking away:

'And that other wound, has it healed?'

'I'm studying how to heal the earth of all sorts of wounds; and as for that . . .' He waved his hand, shifted his tools from his right to his left shoulder and strode on, smiling, heavy and awkward of gait.

1925

The Heart of a Boy

For two summers running the drought had scorched the peasants' fields black. For two years running the cruel east wind had blown from the steppes of Kazakhstan, tousling the dark-brown heads of corn and drying the scanty burning tears from the peasants' eyes as they gazed at the sun-dried steppe. The drought was followed by famine. The boy Aliosha imagined it as an enormous, eyeless man who came striding over the pathless steppe, groping with his hands at the settlements, the villages, the district centres, choking people. And any moment now he would squeeze Aliosha's own heart with his unfeeling hands.

Aliosha had a big, swollen belly, and swollen feet. Touch his livid blue calf with your finger, and first you would have seen a small white dimple, then, slowly, slowly over the hollow the skin would swell into little blisters, and the spot which you had touched with your finger would be flooded for a long time with blood of an earthy colour.

The skin on his nose, ears, cheeks and chin was drawn very tight; it looked like the skin of a withered cherry. His eyes had sunk so deep that the sockets seemed to be empty hollows. He was fourteen years old. He hadn't eaten bread for five months. His body was swelling with hunger.

Early one morning, when the weeds were spreading a honeyed scent along by the wattle fence, when the bees were swinging drunkenly on the small yellow flowers, and the dewy morning was ringing with transparent stillness, Aliosha, swaying in the wind, made his way to the ditch, groaning as he went. It took him a long time to get across it. He sat down by the fence, which was sweating with dew. His head was swimming pleasantly with joy, though he felt sick in the pit of his stomach. His head was swimming with joy because by his stiff blue legs the small, still warm body of a dead baby foal was lying.

Their neighbour's mare had been in foal. They had not

looked after her properly, and in the pasturage the village bull had gored her in the belly, and she had dropped her young. Now it lay, still warm, steaming with blood, by the wattle fence. And Aliosha sat beside it, digging his bony hands into the ground and laughing, laughing.

He tried to pick up the body, but he hadn't the strength. So he went back home and got a knife. By the time he had made his way back to the fence the dogs had gathered on the spot where the foal had been lying, and they were tugging and dragging the rosy meat over the dusty ground. A groan came from Aliosha's twisted lips. Stumbling, waving his knife, he chased the dogs off. Then he collected all the meat, down to the last intestine, and carried it home in two journeys.

Late in the afternoon, after eating some of the stringy meat, Aliosha's black-eyed younger sister died.

His mother lay a long time face downward on the earthen floor; then she got up, turned to Aliosha and whispered with her ashen lips:

'Take her by the feet. . . .'

They picked her up: Aliosha by the feet, his mother by her curly head. They carried her through the orchard to the ditch, and scattered some earth lightly over the body.

Next day the neighbour's boy met Aliosha dragging along the alley, and said, picking his nose and looking away:

'Aliosha, our mare's dropped her foal, and the dogs have eaten it. . . .'

Aliosha leant against a gate-post, but said nothing.

'And the dogs have dug up your sister Niura from the ditch and have eaten out her innards. . . .'

Aliosha turned and walked away silently, not looking back.

Hopping on one leg, the boy shouted after him:

'Mummy says anyone buried without a priest and not in the churchyard will be tortured by the devils in hell. D'you hear, Aliosha?'

A week passed. Aliosha's gums began to fester. When in his ravenous hunger he chewed the resinous bark of an elm tree his teeth wriggled and danced in his mouth, and his throat was clutched with spasms.

63

His mother, who had lain for three days without getting up, whispered to him:

'Aliosha . . . you might go . . . and pull up some spurge in the garden. . . .'

Aliosha's legs were like blades of grass; he looked at them doubtfully as he lay on his back, and said very slowly through his painful, split lips:

'Mummy, I won't get there. . . . The wind'll blow me over.'

That same day Polia, Aliosha's older sister, waited for their rich neighbour, Makarchikha, to go off across the stream to her vegetable plot, watched her yellow kerchief glimmering through the orchards and then climbed into her cottage through the window. She dragged the bench up to the stove and climbed on to it; she drank some cabbage soup straight out of the iron pot, and fished out a potato with her fingers. The food made her drowsy, and she fell asleep just as she was, with her head on the stove and her feet on the bench. Makarchikha returned just before dinner-time; she was a healthy and ill-natured woman. When she saw Polia she squealed and gripped the girl's scattered locks with one hand. Clutching a flat-iron with the other, she silently beat her on the head, the face, on her empty, withered breasts.

From his yard Aliosha saw Makarchikha come out and look around her; then she dragged Polia off the verandah by her feet. The bottom of Polia's skirt was drawn up over her head, and her hair swept the dust and left a bloody trail over the ground.

Through the interlacing of the wattle Aliosha watched without blinking as Makarchikha flung Polia into a disused, half-ruined well and hurriedly threw earth down over her.

The orchards at night are scented with earthy rawness, with nettle heads and the drugging smell of burdocks. Along the weather-beaten fencing the docks guard the path constantly. That night Aliosha went out into the orchard and stood staring for a long time at Makarchikha's yard, at the small, mica windows, at the splashes of moonlight sprinkling the shaggy foliage of the orchard. Then he stole quietly towards the yard gate. The dog tied up under the granary rattled its chain and growled.

'Ssh! Quiet, Serko!' Aliosha pursed his lips and whistled ingratiatingly, and the dog quietened down.

He did not go through the wicket gate, but pushed through the wattle fence and, groping his way, crawled to the underground cellar covered with steppe shrubs and branches. Keeping his ears pricked up, he rattled the chain. The cellar was not padlocked. He lifted the trap-door, and, huddling, climbed down the ladder.

He did not see Makarchikha come running out of the summer kitchen. Tucking up her skirt, she skipped over to the cart standing in the middle of the yard, pulled the tie-bolt out of the front wheel limber and ran to the cellar. She stuck her dishevelled head down through the trap; but Aliosha was standing with his glazed eyes covered with one hand, and, listening to the thumping of his heart, he drank from the ewer of milk without taking breath.

'Ah, you . . . may it choke you! What d'you think you're up to, you son of a bitch?'

The suddenly heavy ewer slipped out of Aliosha's freezing fingers and smashed to pieces against the foot of the ladder.

Makarchikha dropped down into the cellar.

She picked up Aliosha easily by the shoulders, and then silently, her lips tightly pursed, she went out into the alley, made her way along by the fences to the stream and threw his inert body on the mud at the water's edge.

The next day was Trinity Sunday. Makarchikha's floor was strewn with savory and thyme. Early in the morning she milked the cow, drove her off to join the village herd, took out a flower-patterned shawl, put it over her head and went to see Aliosha's mother. The door to the porch was wide open, a cadaverous smell came from the unswept room. She went in. Aliosha's mother was lying on the bed, her legs tucked up, one hand shielding her eyes from the light. Makarchikha crossed herself fervently in front of the sooted ikon.

'What, lying in bed like a lady, this time of day, Anisimovna?' she said.

No answer. Anisimovna's mouth was twisted open, flies

were speckling her cheeks and buzzing hollowly in her mouth. Makarchikha walked across to the bed.

'You've been living well a long time, my dear. . . . To tell the truth I've just dropped in to ask whether you'd sell your hut. You know, my daughter's of marriageable age, I'd like to take a son-in-law. But are you asleep, or what?'

She touched Anisimovna's hand and was burnt by its prickly chill. She groaned and turned to run from the dead woman. But at the door Aliosha was standing with a face whiter than chalk. Smeared with blood and river slime, he clung to the door-latch:

'But I'm still alive, auntie . . . don't kill me . . . I won't any more!'

As dusk was falling Aliosha went along the streets spread with curly carpets of dust, across the square, past the weathered church wall. By the school, under some lowering acacias, he fell in with the priest. He was coming away from the church, and was carrying pasties and salt beef in a sack on his bent back. Twisting his lips, Aliosha said hoarsely:

'For Christ's sake . . .'

'God will give . . .' The priest walked past him, hunched, his feet catching in the edge of his cassock.

Down by the stream the brick sheds and granaries were filled with grain. In one yard was a house roofed with sheet-iron. It was the collection point, No. 32, of the Don Products Committee. Under the overhang of the shed was a field kitchen, two two-wheeled ammunition wagons; sentries and uncleaned bayonet blades were visible by the granaries. The grain guard.

Aliosha waited till the sentry had turned his back, then he dived under the granary (during the morning he had discovered that grain was sifting in a yellow stream through a chink). He gathered up the rough seed in his cupped hands, and chewed greedily. He ate obliviously, but came to himself when he heard a voice behind him:

'Who's that?'

'It's me. . . .'

'And who are you?'

'Aliosha. . . .'

66

'Well, crawl out of there!'

Aliosha rose to his feet, screwed up his eyes and waited for the blow, covering his face with his hands. They stood thus for some time. Then the voice barked in a kindly tone:

'Come to my room, Aliosha. I've got wheat that's cooked.'

Aliosha saw spectacles shining vaguely on a hooked nose, and a smile which didn't seem at all angry. The bespectacled man walked off with long strides, as though on stilts, but the boy hurried after him, stumbling and falling on his hands. In the collection point office, the second door on the right along the passage had a notice: 'Office of Political Commissar Sinitsin'.

They went in. The bespectacled man lit an oil lamp, sat down on a stool with his legs wide apart and very gently pushed a pot of boiled wheat and a half bottle of sunflower-seed oil under Aliosha's nose. He watched as the boy's jaws worked and the muscles rose and fell on his cheeks. Then he got up and took away the pot. But the boy clung to the rim with his warty fingers. His head shaking, he sobbed:

'Do you grudge it me, greedy?'

'No, I don't, you little idiot. But if you guzzle too much you'll snuff out.'

The next morning Aliosha arrived in the collection office yard as soon as it was daylight. He sat down on the broken steps and waited till sunrise for the door with the notice 'Office of Political Commissar Sinitsin' to open and the man with spectacles to appear.

The sun was streaming over the brick sheds before the man got up. He came out on to the verandah, and wrinkled up his nose:

'Is it you making that stink, Aliosha?'

'I want something to eat,' the boy said hoarsely, gazing up at the spectacles.

'We'll be making some porridge directly, but . . . all the same, you do stink, Aliosha Popovich.'

Aliosha said, frankly and to the point:

'Makarchikha beat me, and now I'm hot, and I've got maggots in my head. . . .'

The Commissar turned pale, and questioned him:

67

'You've got maggots?'

'In the head. They're biting hard. . . .'

Aliosha took the cap of tow and festering blood off his head, and the spectacles stared at the round, suppurating wound. He saw the beady little maggot heads poking out of the matter, and groaned as he leaned over the balustrade.

Aliosha grew bold, and he said:

'I tell you what . . . you pick them out with a piece of stick, and then pour paraffin into the wound. . . . The paraffin will kill the maggots, won't it?'

The Commissar got a pointed stick and picked the slippery maggots out, while Aliosha huddled down and hopped from foot to foot to bear the pain. And thus a friendship developed between the two of them. Aliosha went every day to the collection point office; he ate oat gruel from a mug, drank vegetable oil, ate a lot and greedily, and was always fearfully conscious of an inquisitive yet kindly gaze fixed on him.

Beyond the pasturage, beyond the green wall of rustling maize stalks the rye was ripening. The ears swelled and were filled with firm, milky grain. Every day Aliosha drove the collection point horses out past the grain into the steppe to graze. He did not hobble them, but let them rove over the wormwooded hollows, over the grey feather-grass, while he wandered into the corn. The full-grown stalks of the rye readily huddled together to make way for him, and he lay down very carefully, trying not to crush the grain. He lay on his back and rubbed ears of corn in his palms and ate the grain till he was almost sick; it was soft and scented, filled with white milk.

One day he drove the horses into the steppe and spent some time fussing round a capricious bucking little mare, trying to pick the burrs out of her mane and to clean the dry scabs off her body. The mare bared her blackened teeth and tried to bite him or push him with her hindquarters. Aliosha was artful: he seized her by the tail. But at that moment he heard someone behind him say:

'Ah, Aliosha! Enough of your villainous goings on! Would you like to work for me, as my help? I'll keep you in victuals, and I'll find you a pair of boots of some sort.'

Aliosha let go of the mare's tail and looked round. One of the village's rich farmers, Ivan Alexeev, was standing a little way off and smiling as he watched Aliosha.

'Come and work for me. Will you? The grub'll be all it should be, really good. . . . I've got milk and other things. . . .'

Aliosha did not stop to think; delighted to have the chance of work and food, he burst out:

'I'll come, Ivan Alexeev.'

'Well, bring your things along this evening.' And Ivan Alexeev turned and went off, his faded shirt glimmering in the maize.

A naked man is dressed when he puts on his belt. Aliosha had no family or relations. His only property was stones; his mother had sold their hut and yard to neighbours before she died: the hut for nine cupped handfuls of flour, the yard for wheat. And Makarchikha had bought the orchard for a jug of milk. All Aliosha possessed was his father's old coat and his mother's shabby felt boots. He brought the horses back from grazing, then went off to Ivan Alexeev's yard. The housewife put down some sacking by the summer kitchen, and the family sat down on the ground and ate their supper. Aliosha's nostrils were tickled by the smell of boiled lamb. He swallowed his spittle and stood close by, crumpling his cap in his hands and thinking: 'The mistress might at least let me sit down to supper.' But things didn't work out that way. The woman bawled and grumbled, and banged the iron pots about:

'You've brought us another idler! He'll guzzle more than he earns. For God's sake send him away, Alexeev. We don't need him in times like these.'

'Shut your mouth, woman! There are two holes: learn how to stop them both!' Ivan Alexeev said, wiping his beard with his sleeve.

And that ended the conversation.

It was not the first time Aliosha had worked. He took after his father, he was a glutton for work. He had been a herdsman at the age of seven, and had twisted the bullocks' tails properly.

He lived with the Alexeevs for three days, grew accustomed to the work, rode to the windmill with his master's daughter-in-law and stooked the hay as it was mowed. He made himself comfortable at night under the overhang of the shed. The very first night the master came out to him, belching and stinking of onions, and said:

'If you think of smoking here, you bitch's udder, I'll twist your head off your neck with my own hands. Don't let me catch you!'

'I don't smoke, uncle.'

'All right, then, but watch out!'

He went away, but Aliosha couldn't get to sleep. Nor did he sleep any better the following night. His arms and legs ached with working in the field, his back was swollen with sores, and sleep simply would not come. Early in the morning of the third day he ran along to the collection point office. The spectacled man was washing himself on the verandah, grunting and snorting.

'Hello, Aliosha, where've you been?' he asked.

'I've hired myself out as a labourer.'

'Who to?'

'Ivan Alexeev; he lives on the edge of the village.'

'Well, brother, come along this evening. We'll have a talk about it.'

After he had watered the animals that evening Aliosha went off to the office. The Commissar was rummaging among some books.

'D'you know your letters, Alexei?' he asked the boy.

'I went to the day school. I can sign my name.'

'Come with me.'

They went along the passage. At the end was a door, and on it was written in chalk: 'Young Communists' Club'. So much Aliosha managed to spell out. But it was strange and meant nothing to him. The spectacled man went in, and Aliosha shyly followed him. In the small room were portraits, a faded red flag and a few lads whom he knew. They were reading aloud from a book; they glanced up as the door creaked, then bent over the table again, to listen. Aliosha also started listening. They were reading something about how masters should hire labourers, and various other things. Aliosha did not get back to the yard from the club till midnight. For a long time he tossed and turned on the ragged sacking. All night, right till dawn came, the moon, lying on its back, stared insolently into his eyes.

Ivan Alexeev said to Aliosha:

'You look out and keep hard at it, you son of a bitch. The moment I catch you idling I'll turn you out of my yard. You can go and snuff out in the street.'

Aliosha helped with the mowing, and the threshing, and saw to the cattle, while Ivan Alexeev thrust his hands behind his fringed woollen girdle and walked smirking about his yard.

One holiday his neighbour called out to him:

'You're doing well, Ivan Alexeev!'

'Praise be!'

'Have you lost every scrap of conscience?'

'What d'you mean?'

'Why, the way you're behaving, it's disgusting. You're working that Aliosha like a horse. You'll kill the boy. You'll be taking a sin on your soul.'

'You mind your own business, neighbour, and don't go staring your eyes out at another man's yard. You can go to hell!' He turned his back and strode off with a measured rolling gait. But when he got round the corner of the shed he turned, chewed his beard with his strong yellow teeth and swore violently. But for the moment he concealed his fury at his neighbour at the bottom of his heart.

From then on he took his revenge on his poor neighbour, who had no horse. He chased the man's wretched cow out of his stubble, and kept it tied up without food for two days. And he made Aliosha work even harder, beating him mercilessly for the least thing.

Aliosha had a good mind to complain to the man in spectacles; but he was afraid to, fearing that if Ivan Alexeev discovered it he would turn him out. During those brief, stifling nights under the overhang of the shed he wet his pillow with bitter tears. But each evening, as soon as he had driven the cattle back from watering, he stole off through the threshing floor, huddling against the wattle fence, and ran to the club. Every evening he met the man in spectacles. The Commissar smiled

71

as he looked at the boy over the rims of his spectacles, and clapped him on the back. One Sunday Aliosha went along to the club before it was dark. The small club-room was crowded, everybody was carrying a rifle, and at his waist the spectacled man had a holster with a twisted strap, and something shining which looked rather like a small bottle.

When he saw Aliosha he came across to him with a smile:

'Bandits have entered our district, Alexei. If they occupy the district centre you come to us, to defend the club.'

Aliosha badly wanted to ask what it all meant, but in front of so many people he was too shy. Next morning he had to oil the mowing machine. Looking across to the summer kitchen, he saw his master coming out. Aliosha's inside went cold: Alexeev's brows were knitted, he was tugging at his beard as he came. It looked as though something had gone wrong somewhere, and the boy was afraid of his master, who could be brutally violent. Alexeev came up to the mowing machine:

'Where do you go off to at night, you little reptile?'

Aliosha did not answer. The can of oil trembled in his hands.

'Where d'you go to, I ask?'

'To the club . . .'

'Ah! To the club! But haven't you ever had a taste of this, damn you?'

The master's fist was covered with yellow hair, and was as heavy as a weight. He struck the boy on the back of the neck, and Aliosha's legs gave way under him; he fell chest downward on to the mower, and sparks flew like millet husks from his eyes.

'You'll get out of your habit of wandering about! If you don't, you can clear out to the devil, and don't leave the stink of you behind!'

As he harnessed the horses to the mower, he roared:

'I took him in out of pity, but he goes hobnobbing with those sons of bitches. And later on when another government comes they'll make a fuss because of you, you snake. Well, you go there again and I'll give you something to remember it by.'

Aliosha had big, widely spaced teeth, and he was simple-hearted, he had never been angry with anyone in all his life. His mother had said to him sometimes:

'Ah, Aliosha, you'll be lost if I die. The chickens will bury you under their turds. And who do you take after? Your father was beaten to death in the mines because of his ways. . . . He was a nail for every hole. . . . But as for you, the other lads all take it out of you, and when you grow up you'll always be getting the hiding.'

Aliosha had a good heart; had he any right to be angry with his master, who was giving him his food? He got up, and recovered a little. But his master started beating him again, because he had spilt the oil when he fell on the mower. Somehow the boy got through till the evening; then he lay down under his sacking and buried his head in a pillow.

It was still dark when he woke up. He heard horse hoofs clattering along the alley; they came to a halt at the gate. The ring fastening the wicket gate rattled. He heard steps, and a tap at the window.

'Master!' a voice called softly, in an undertone.

Aliosha listened; the door was flung open, Ivan Alexeev came on to the verandah. He and the stranger talked together quietly for some time.

'It would be as well to give the horses some food,' the words reached Aliosha under the shed.

He raised his head, and saw two men in greatcoats lead saddled horses into the yard and tie them to the verandah rail. His master went with one of them towards the threshing floor. As they passed the shed Alexeev looked under the over-hang and quietly asked:

'Are you asleep, Aliosha?'

Aliosha lay quietly, snoring gently through his nose. But he listened tensely, raising his head a little.

'I've got a lad living with me . . . Unreliable . . .' Alexeev remarked.

Some five minutes later the threshing-floor wicket creaked, and Alexeev brought back an armful of hay. He was followed by one of the strangers, who was clattering a sabre and tripping over his long greatcoat. Alexei heard a hoarse, quiet voice:

'Have they got machine-guns?'

73

'Where'd they get them from? Two troops of Reds are quartered in the office yard. . . . And that's the lot. . . . Then there's the Political Commissar, and the scalesmen. . . .'

'We'll call on them as guests tomorrow at midnight. . . . And we'll take them all out to the government forest. . . . If we catch them by surprise we'll finish them all off.'

A horse began to neigh by the verandah, and another man in a greatcoat shouted angrily:

'Keep quiet, you brute!'

There was the sound of a blow, and the clatter of dancing hoofs.

In the greying darkness just before dawn the two horsemen rode out of Ivan Alexeev's yard and made off at a swinging trot along the road towards the government forest.

At breakfast next morning Alexei ate hardly anything, and sat with his head drooping. His master looked at him suspiciously:

'Why aren't you eating?'

'I've got a headache.'

He forced himself to sit and wait till the meal was over. Then he stole away through the threshing floor, sprang over the wattle fence and trotted off to the office. He burst like a wind into the Political Commissar's room, slammed the door behind him and stood just inside, pressing his hands to his beating heart.

'Where've you come from, Aliosha, bursting in like that?'

The boy told a confused story of the nocturnal visitors, and related the snatches of conversation he had overheard. Sinitsin listened, not missing a word. At the end he got up and said kindly to Aliosha:

'You stay here.' He went out.

Aliosha remained sitting in the Commissar's room for a good half hour. The wasps buzzed angrily at the window, strands of sunlight strayed over the floor. Hearing voices in the yard, he looked out of the window. The spectacled man was standing with two Red Army men on the verandah, and they had Ivan Alexeev between them. Alexeev's beard was quivering and his lips were trembling.

74

'Somebody's said something to you out of spite . . .' he muttered.

'We'll see about that!'

Aliosha had never seen the spectacled man looking like that before. His eyebrows had met over his nose, his eyes were glittering sternly under his glasses. He unfastened the door of the brick shed, stood to one side and said harshly to Ivan Alexeev:

'Get inside!'

Aliosha's master stooped and went into the shed. The door was slammed behind him.

'Now watch! Like this: and then, one, two and the cartridge case is ejected. And you put the new cartridge in here.'

The rifle bolt rattled in the spectacled man's hand; he looked at Aliosha over his glasses, and smiled.

That evening darkness settled over the village like a puddle of tar. The Red Army men lay in a line on the square by the church wall. Aliosha lay at the Commissar's side. His rifle had a smelly strap, and the evening dew was making the barrel sweat.

At midnight, close to the cemetery on the village outskirts, a dog began to bark, then another. The next moment the crisp thud of horse hoofs reached the ears of the waiting Red Army men. The man in spectacles rose on one knee, took aim at the far end of the street, and shouted:

'Company . . . fire!'

The rifles rattled out.

From behind the wall came the terrified mutter of the echo.

Once, twice, Aliosha shot home the rifle bolt, ejected the spent cartridge and again heard the hoarse shout: 'Company, fire!'

From the end of the street came shots, swearing, the squeal of horses. Aliosha listened as a rifle bullet sang over his head.

A moment or two later another bullet smacked into the wall some two feet above the boy's head; it sprinkled bits of brick over him. At the far end of the street he saw a few tiny sparks of rifle fire, then heard the thunder of horse hoofs in disorderly retreat. The spectacled man sprang to his feet and shouted:

'Follow me!'

75

They started running. Aliosha's mouth felt hot and dry, his heart seemed too big for his chest. At the end of the street the man in spectacles stumbled over a dead horse and fell. Aliosha, running at his side, saw two men ahead of them leap over a wattle fence and run across a yard. A door slammed. A bolt was shot home.

'There they are! Two of them ran into the hut,' the boy shouted.

Limping on his grazed leg, the Commissar came up to Aliosha. The yard was surrounded. The Red Army men lay down in the orchard with its damp currant bushes, behind the cemetery wall, and huddled down in the ditch. The men in the hut opened fire from windows barricaded with pillows; in the intervals between the firing the besiegers heard the swearing of hoarse, breathless voices. Then there was silence.

The Commissar and Aliosha were lying side by side. Just before dawn, as the raw darkness began to roll away through the orchard, the Commissar shouted without raising his head:

'Hey, you in there! Surrender! Or we'll throw a grenade.'

Two shots came from the hut. The Commissar signalled with his hand:

'At the windows, fire!'

A dry, distinct salvo of shots. Another, and another. Hiding behind the thick adobe walls, the two men inside the hut fired only occasionally, running from window to window.

'Aliosha, you're shorter than me; crawl along the ditch to that shed, and throw this grenade at the door. . . . We'll be hours winkling them out otherwise. . . . Here, look! You slip back this ring. Then throw it at once, or it'll kill you.'

The Commissar had untied the thing that looked like a bottle from his belt. He gave it to Aliosha. Crouching down and falling on the damp earth, the boy crawled along; above him, above the ditch, the bullets scythed down the weedy scrub, and sprinkled a chilly dew over him. He crawled up to the shed, slipped back the ring and took aim at the door. But the door creaked, shook and was flung open. Two men strode across the threshold: the leader was carrying a girl perhaps four years old in his arms; in the early morning twilight the white patch of her shirt was clearly visible. Blood was streaming from the torn cossack trousers of the second man; clinging to the door latch, he halted with his head twisted sideways.

'We surrender. Don't shoot. You'll kill the child.'

Aliosha saw a woman run to the door; she placed herself in front of the child, wringing her hands and screaming. The boy looked back, and saw the Commissar rise to his knees; Sinitsin was as white as a sheet, he looked around fearfully.

The boy realized what he must do. His teeth were big and widely spaced, and that always indicates a soft heart. So his mother used to say. He lay down on top of the gleaming, bottle-shaped grenade, and covered his face with his hands.

But the Commissar dashed over to Aliosha, pushed him aside with his foot, and, with a grim look on his face, snatched up the grenade and flung it away. A second later a fiery column flew up high above the garden; Aliosha heard a thunderous roar, then the Commissar's groaning cry. He felt something stinking of sulphur burn his chest; a thick prickly film settled into his eyes.

When he recovered consciousness he saw the spectacled man's face, grey with sleepless nights, bent over him.

He tried to raise his head, but his chest was seared with pain; he began to groan, then to laugh.

'I'm still alive. . . . I didn't die. . . .'

'And you won't die, Aliosha. You mustn't die now. Here, look at this!'

The Commissar was holding a card with a number in his hand; he raised it to Aliosha's eyes, and he read:

' "Member of the Young Communist League, Aliosha Popov . . ." Understand, Aliosha?'

'A bit of the grenade hit you an inch from your heart,' he told the boy. 'But now we've got you on the road to being well again, and your heart can go on beating . . . to the benefit of the Workers' and Peasants' Government. . . .'

He squeezed Aliosha's hand; and through the dim, sweating glasses of the spectacles the boy saw something he had never seen before: two small bright tears, and a wry, quivering smile.

1925

77

The Crooked Path

It seemed not so very long ago that Niura was an awkward gawky girl. She waddled, pointing out her toes and swinging her long arms clumsily; whenever she met a stranger she would step aside and glance rather shyly with embarrassment with her black eyes from under her kerchief. But now Vasily saw a shapely, full-breasted young woman coming towards him. She looked straight ahead as she walked, the tiniest of smiles on her lips. And Vasily felt as though a warm spring wind were blowing into his face.

He screwed up his eyes for a moment, then turned to look back after her; he followed her with his eyes till she went round a corner, then put his horse into a trot. As he unbridled his horse at the watering spot he smiled, recalling the meeting. For some reason he could still see Niura's hands, gently yet firmly clutching the flowered yoke across her shoulders, and the green buckets swinging to the rhythm of her walk. After that first meeting he sought every opportunity of falling in with her; he deliberately rode down to the stream along the farthest street, in order to pass her father's hut. And when he saw her across the fence or in the square of the window his joy brought a warmth to his heart; he pulled on the reins to slow up his horse.

On the Friday of that same week he rode out to the meadow to take a look at the hay. After the rain it was steaming, and was giving off a sweet raw scent. He noticed Niura over by a hayrick. She was walking along with her skirt tucked up, waving a switch. He rode across to her

'Hello, beautiful!'

'Hello, if you're not joking!' And she smiled.

He sprang off his horse and threw the reins over its neck.

'What are you looking for, Niura?'

'A calf has strayed. You haven't seen it at all, have you?'

'The herd went past me to the village some time ago, but I didn't see your calf with it.'

He took out his tobacco pouch and twisted himself a cigarette. As he licked the edge of the scrap of newspaper he asked her:

'When did you manage to get such a healthy look, my girl? It's not so long since you were playing buck and four stones in the sand. And now, just look at you.'

The corners of Niura's eyes wrinkled up with her smile. She answered:

'That's just the way things go, Vasily Timofeevich. After all, it wasn't so long ago that you were running off into the steppe without any trousers on to catch starlings. And now I expect you knock your head against the lintel of your hut.'

'Why don't you get married?' Vasily struck a match as he asked, and drew avidly at his home-grown tobacco.

Niura sighed jokingly, and threw out her hands in a gesture of distress:

'No one's come along.'

'But what's wrong with me?' Vasily tried to smile. But the smile was twisted, and it didn't please him. He recalled his reflection in the looking-glass: his cheeks deeply pitted from an attack of smallpox long ago, his hair curly and like a brigand's, falling over his forehead.

'You're just a bit pock-marked, otherwise you wouldn't be at all bad,' she answered.

'You wouldn't have to drink from my face,' Vasily retorted, flushing.

Niura smiled faintly, and said, waving the switch:

'That's very true! Well, then, if you like me, send the matchmakers along.'

She turned and went off towards the village. But Vasily spent some time sitting under the rick, rubbing a sweet-scented leaf of hedge parsley between his palms, and thinking: 'Is she laughing at me, the bitch, or isn't she?'

From the stream and the forest came a freezing chill.

A low mist rolled over the mown grass, fumbled with its swollen grey feelers at the prickly stubble and womanlike wrapped around the steaming ricks. Beyond the three poplars, whither the sun had set for the night, the sky blossomed with

79

wild rose, and the steeply banked clouds looked like faded petals.

Vasily's family consisted of his mother and sister. Their hut, on the outskirts of the village, had rooted firmly and dignifiedly in the ground; their farmstead was small. A horse and a cow were all their livestock. Vaska's father had lived poorly.

And so on the Sunday, as she wrapped herself in a flower-patterned shawl, Vaska's mother said to him:

'My son, I've got nothing against it; Niura's a hard-working girl and not at all stupid. Only, we're poor, her father won't give her to you. . . . You know how obstinate Osip is.'

Vasily was pulling on his boots, and he said nothing; but his cheeks flushed crimson: whether from the strain (the boots were painfully tight) or for some other reason.

His mother wiped her dry pale lips with the end of her shawl, and added:

'I'll go and see Osip, Vaska; but we'll be put to shame if he shows the matchmaker the door. The whole village will be laughing at us. . . .' She was silent for a moment or two, then she whispered:

'Well, I'm off.'

'Yes, you go, mother.' Vasily stood up, smiling wanly.

Wiping her brow with her sleeve, for she was hot and sweating, Vasily's mother said:

'You have goods, Osip Maximovich, and we have a purchaser. . . . That's why I've come. . . . What do you think?'

Sitting on the bench, Osip twisted his beard and, blowing the dust off the bench beside him, delivered his opinion:

'You see, it's like this, Timofeevna. . . . Possibly I mightn't be against it . . . Vasily's a very suitable lad for our farm. . . . Only we're not giving our daughter in marriage. . . . It's early yet for her to wed. . . . Giving birth to children's a simple matter. . . .'

'In that case excuse me for bothering you.'

Vasily's mother pursed her lips and, rising from the chest on which she had been sitting, bowed to Osip.

'It wasn't any bother,' he answered. 'Why are you in such a hurry, Timofeevna? You could spend the afternoon with us?'

'I'm afraid not. I must hurry back home. . . . Good-bye, Osip Maximovich.'

'God be with you! . . . And good riddance!' Osip barked without getting up, as Vaska's mother slammed the door.

Niura's mother came in from the yard. As she poured sunflower seeds into a frying pan to roast, she asked:

'What did Timofeevna want?'

Osip spat and swore:

'She came to propose a match for her pock-marked son. You'll find stinking bugs wherever there are people! She can chop up her own wood! A fine matchmaker she!' He waved his hand in disgust. 'Nothing but trouble!'

All the grain had been harvested. The threshing floors, rusty and ragged-looking with the stacks of unthreshed rye, gazed out expectantly over the fence. They were waiting for the farmers to start threshing. The men gathered with their rakes around the threshing machines, bawling in hoarse, strained tones:

'Come on! Come on!'

Autumn crept over the land with rain and a dreary mist.

Every morning the steppe was covered with mist like a horse with scabs. The sun, uncertainly appearing and disappearing through the clouds, seemed wretched and impotent. Only the forests, still looking fresh despite the summer's heat, self-satisfiedly rustled their leaves as green and supple as in spring.

The rains came frequently, one after another in a long succession, through the slippery, unpleasant mist. For their own good reasons the wild geese flew westward, and the ricks, settling down and covered with a brownish must, resembled a sick man.

The unploughed soil was sunk in an early autumn doze. The meadows were brilliantly green with the aftermath, but their gleam was deceptive, like the flush on the face of a man eaten up with consumption.

Only Vaska blossomed with joy like a vigorous thistle, for he was seeing Niura every day. He met her either down by the stream or during the village merry-making at night. He began to lose his wits, he lost his sap; the work dropped from his hands.

And then suddenly, one cloudy autumnal day, in the late afternoon the accordion, which had been whining and shrinking like a homeless whelp, broke into full-throated, wide-bellowed music, and panted with laughter.

Grishka, the secretary of the village's Young Communist group, came running to Vaska's yard. When he saw Vasily he waved his hands, and his smile split his cheeks in two.

'What are you grinning like that for: found a fortune, or what?' Vaska asked him.

'Cut it out, you idiot! What fortune?' Grishka stopped for breath, then fired at Vasily: 'Our year has been called up into the army. Muster in three days' time!'

But as for Vaska, the news was like someone breaking a stake over his head. His first thought was: 'But how about Niura?' He rubbed his forehead with his hand, and asked thickly:

'What are you so joyful about?'

Grishka's eyebrows shot right up to his hair:

'Well, why not? We're going into the army, you fool. We'll see the world. What joy can anyone have around here, apart from dung? But in the army, my boy, we'll be studying. . . .'

Vaska turned on his heels and went off to the threshing floor, with his head hanging, not looking back.

That night Vaska waited for Niura by a gap in the fence of Osip's orchard. She was late in turning up. She was wearing her father's coat to protect her from the cold, but even so she was shivering in the damp night air.

Vaska looked into her eyes, but he could see nothing. She seemed not to have any eyes; there was a black emptiness in the sockets.

'I've got to go into the army, Niura.'

'So I've heard.'

'Well, but how about you? Will you wait for me? You won't marry someone else?'

Niura laughed quietly; her voice and her laugh seemed unfamiliar, strange.

'I've already told you I shan't take any notice of father or mother, I'll go with you. And I would. . . . But not now. . . . It's no joke waiting two years. Maybe you'll find a town girl there, while I remain a maiden here! There aren't any fools around, these days. . . . Ask someone else, maybe you'll find a girl willing to wait for you. . . .'

Vaska pleaded with her for a long time, stammering, his head twitching nervously. He implored her, he assured her, he swore by God. But Niura snapped the dry twig she was holding and answered resolutely, with one curt, callous word:

'No. No.'

At last he shouted furiously, panting:

'All right then, you bitch! You won't come to me, but you'll be quick to go to someone else. But if you do take another man you won't escape my hands.'

'They'll make your hands short, they won't reach me!' Niura flared up.

'I'll get you somehow!'

He jumped over the fence without saying good-bye, and went off through the orchard, treading the fallen yellow leaves into the mud.

Next morning he put a hunk of bread in the pocket of his sheepskin jacket, and without telling his mother poured some flour into a bag, then went off to ask a forester to put him up.

His head was heavy after his sleepless night, his swollen eyes watered and his whole body ached painfully but pleasantly. Carefully avoiding the puddles, he went up to the verandah. The forester was drawing water from a well.

'D'you want me, Vasily?'

'Yes, Semion Mikhailich. . . . Before going off to do my service I'd like to have a last hunt.'

Bending sideways under the weight of the full bucket, the forester came across to Vaska and, narrowing his eyes, asked:

'Did you get anything last Sunday?'

'Just one leveret.'

They went into the hut. The forester put the bucket down on the bench, then brought out an ancient fowling piece. Moodily staring into the corner, Vaska asked:

'It's a rifle I need. . . . I saw signs of a fox in Sleepy Ravine.'

'I can lend you a rifle, only I haven't any cartridges.'

'I've got some of my own.'

'Then you can have it. Drop in on your way back, and tell me all about it. Well, good luck to you!' the smiling forester called after Vaska as he went off.

In the forest some three miles from the village, at a spot where a ravine washed by the autumnal floods rises upward into steep gulleys, under an overturned tree Vaska dug out a small cave with only room for a wolf in the reddish, oily clay. He lived there for four whole days.

In the daytime there was a warm freshness, an invigorating and intoxicating scent at the bottom of the forest ravine; the oak leaves smelt strongly as they rotted. At night, under the slanting, dancing rays of the horned moon the ravine seemed bottomless; somewhere above him he heard rustles, the creaking of branches, a vague alarming sound as though someone were stealing along the winding edge of the ravine and looking down into its depths. Occasionally after midnight the young wolf cubs called to one another.

During the day he left the ravine, walking sluggishly on his stiff legs, through the dense, prickly thorns, through the bare hazel bushes, across the gullys, a quarter filled with orange-coloured leaves. And when, through the fading curtain of the thin foliage that still remained on the bushes, he saw the glimmering pale green surface of the river, and beyond it the whitewashed cubes of the village houses, he felt a numb pain somewhere around his heart. He lay a long time on the steep bank of the river, concealed in the brushwood undergrowth, watching as the women came down to the stream for water. On the second day he saw his mother, and felt like calling to her; but a cart drove out from a side street. The Cossack driving waved his knout and gazed in the direction of the stream.

The very first night, when he lay down on a heap of dry,

84

rustling leaves, he did not close his eyes till first light. He lay thinking, realizing that he had not taken the right road, he was on a crooked path. He must tread that path for good or ill together with the bad lads on the broad high-road. And he realized that now he would have everybody against him: Niura, and the lads of his own call-up, who had gone off to join the army to the strains of the accordion. They would do their service, and they would stand in defence of the Soviets if necessary. But who would defend him, Vaska?

In the forest, under the fallen tree, baited like a hunted wolf, he would die from a bullet fired by one of his fellow villagers. He, Vaska, the son of a shepherd, and the born son by blood of the poor people's government.

The east was barely lightening with a lilac streak when, leaving the rifle in the ravine, he went off to the village, hurrying faster and faster.

'I'll go and give myself up. Let them arrest me. They'll put me in prison, but at least I'll be among people. I can stand it from my own folk.' So the painful, burning thought beat through his head. He ran as far as the river. But there he came to a halt. Beyond the sand, beyond the farmyard fences the chimneys were smoking, cattle were bellowing. His back went prickly, as though ants were crawling over it right down to his heels.

'They'll give me three years. . . . No, I won't go . . .'

He turned sharply and went back into the forest, twisting and confusing his tracks like an old vixen dodging the hunters.

By the sixth day he had finished the flour he had brought from home. He waited for nightfall, threw the rifle over his shoulder and quietly, trying to avoid stepping on the fallen twigs and boughs in case they should crack under his feet, he went down to the stream. He walked along to the ford. There were wheel tracks on the damp granular sand. He waded across and came by back paths to Osip's threshing floor. Through the bare branches of the apple trees he saw a light in the window of the hut.

He came to a halt; his longing to see Niura was almost a pain, he wanted to tell her, to fling his reproaches in her face.

85

For it was because of her he had become a deserter, because of her he was perishing in the forest.

He sprang over the fence, ran through the orchard and on to the verandah. He rattled the latch; the door was not bolted. He entered the porch; the warmth of the dwelling struck him in the face and made his head swim.

Niura's mother was kneading dough for dumplings; as she heard the door creak she turned, and dropped the tray, groaning faintly. Osip, who was sitting at the table, grunted, and Niura half screamed and fled into the bedroom.

'You're in good health!' Vaska said hoarsely.

'Praise be!' Osip stammered thickly.

Without taking off his cap, Vaska went into the bedroom. Niura was sitting on the chest, her knees were trembling.

'Aren't you glad to see me, Niura? Why don't you speak to me?' He sat down beside her on the chest, and stood the rifle on its butt beside him.

'What have I got to be glad about?' Niura faltered in a whisper. She clapped her hands and, holding back her tears, demanded: 'Go away, for God's sake! The militia have arrived from the district centre; they're searching for illicit vodka stills. . . . They'll find you. . . . Go, Vaska! Have some pity for me!'

'You had a lot of pity for me . . . didn't you?'

Vaska had hardly closed the bedroom door behind him when Osip winked at his wife and, glancing sidelong in the direction of the bedroom, where Niura was breathlessly whispering, he grunted:

'Run along to Semion. . . . The militia have been put up in his place. Bring them here at once.'

Niura's mother noiselessly opened the front door and slipped through the yard like a black shadow.

Swallowing his spittle with difficulty, Vaska asked:

'Get me a piece of dumpling, Niura. . . . I haven't eaten for two days.'

But as the girl got up the door from the kitchen was flung open; in the open doorway Niura's mother stood, holding a lamp. Her kerchief had slipped awry; sweaty strands of hair hung over her forehead. She squealed rather than shouted:

'Comrade militia-men, seize him, the son of a bitch! There he is!'

The militia-man gazing over her shoulder was about to stride into the bedroom. But Vaska swiftly snatched up his rifle, swung the butt at the lamp, sprang across to the window, pushed open the frame and jumped out, falling heavily on to the fence.

For a moment his face was scorched with the cold. From inside the hut came a hubbub, women's screams, the porch door banged.

He jumped nimbly over the fence and, picking up his rifle, ran in great bounds towards the threshing floor. Behind him he heard running feet, and shouts:

'Halt, Vaska! Halt, or I'll fire!'

By the voice he recognized the militia-man, Proshin. As he ran he threw up his rifle, swung round and fired without taking aim. Behind him he heard the distinct crack of a pistol. As he sprang across the threshing-floor fencing, he felt a burning pain in his left shoulder, as though someone had given him a hard blow with a hot stick. Mastering his pain, he shot back the rifle bolt and ejected the spent cartridge case. He pushed in a fresh cartridge and, aiming at the first form he saw glimmering in the gaps between the apple trees, pulled the trigger. Almost at once he heard Proshin quietly exclaim in a fading tone:

'The dog . . . in my belly . . . Oh, the pain!'

He ran through the ford, not conscious of the cold water. The second militia-man came slowly after him. Turning round, Vaska saw the dark edges of the man's greatcoat blown apart by the wind, and the pistol clutched in his hand. Bullets whistled past Vaska.

He clambered up the steep bank, turned and sent a bullet after the militia-man as he turned back from the stream. Then, unbuttoning his shirt collar, he pressed his lips to the wound. He sucked the warm salty blood for some time, then chewed some gritty earth, laid it on the wound, and, feeling an uninvited cry rising in his throat, clenched his teeth hard.

87

In the early twilight of the following afternoon, he wandered down to the stream and lay in the undergrowth. His shoulder was swollen and a livid blue colour; his shirt had stuck to the wound; the pain was numbed somewhat, and he felt it only when he moved his left arm.

He lay thus for a long time, spitting out the saliva that continually flooded into his mouth. His head felt as empty as if he were drunk. He was so hungry that he felt faint; he chewed the bark off some fallen twigs, then spat it out, staring at the green bubbles of spittle.

Women came down to the stream from the village, drew up water in buckets and returned, swaying with the weight. Just before darkness fell a woman came out of a side street and made towards the river. Groaning with the pain that unexpectedly pierced his left shoulder, Vaska rose on his elbow and furiously gripped his cold rifle barrel.

It was Niura's mother coming down to the stream. Her fluffy kerchief was drawn down right over her eyes. She seemed to be in a hurry. With trembling fingers Vaska released the safety catch. Wiping his eyes, he gazed fixedly. Yes, it was she. The bright yellow jacket that Niura's mother wore, the only one in the village.

With a hunter's precision Vaska brought the head in its fluffy kerchief into his rifle sight.

'You bitch, I'll give it you for blabbing on me. . . .'

His shot rang out. The woman dropped the bucket and ran back towards the yards, without a cry.

'Oh, damn! I've missed!'

Once more the yellow jacket danced in the rifle sight. At the second shot Niura's mother slowly sank down on to the sand and lay in a huddled heap.

Vaska unhurriedly waded across the stream and, carrying his rifle slung on his arm, went up to the body.

He bent down. He caught the hot scent of woman's sweat. Then he saw the open jacket, and under it the torn shirt collar. The gap revealed the swelling rosy nipple of a white breast, and below it a jagged wound and a crimson patch of blood that blossomed over the shirt like a wild tulip.

He glanced under the kerchief drawn down over the forehead.

88

His eyes caught the gaze of Niura's fading eyes, looking straight at him. She had slipped on her mother's jacket to come and fetch water.

He cried out, aghast at what he had done. Then, dropping beside the small motionless body huddled on the ground, he howled with a long, dreary, wolfish howl.

But already Cossacks armed with stakes were running out from the village. Beside the foremost man ran a big shaggy dog, circling and twisting like bindweed. As it ran it yapped and danced round the man, trying to lick him on his beard.

1925

The Woman who had Two Husbands

On the rise beyond the widely spaced telegraph poles the forests huddle in bristling ridges: the Kachalovka, Ataman and Rogozhinska woods. A single dry gully, overgrown with thorns, thrusts into the little village of Kachalovka, and the small, low huts of the settlement crawl up almost to the buildings of the Kachalovka collective farm.

Arseny Kliukvin, the chairman of the collective farm, stood with legs straddled and his body leaning slightly forward. The wind flapped his unbelted shirt, and beads of sweat ran down from his forehead over his nose. At his side was old Artiom, standing with one hairy hand to his eyes, watching as beyond the smelly hillocks of the marmot warrens a tractor broke the black, virgin soil into gleaming clods. Since its start first thing that morning it had turned over eleven acres. Today was its first trial. In his joy Arseny felt a resinous dryness in his throat; he watched the arched back of the tractor till it reached the end of the ploughing area, and then, licking his hot brown lips, remarked to his companion:

'How's that for a machine, daddy Artiom?'

But the old man, grunting and groaning as he stumbled over the rough furrow, crushed a clod of the greasy earth in his brown gnarled hand as he walked, rubbed it on his palm and then, turning to Arseny, flung his ancient cap down on the scarred ploughland and cried out tearfully:

'I'm too ashamed to be able to say. Fifty years I've worked with a bullock, and a bullock with me. . . . You ploughed during the day, you fed it at night and you never had any sleep. . . . And every winter you went through a lean time. . . . But how am I ever to get through this?'

The old man pointed his knout at the tractor, waved one

hand bitterly and, clamping his cap down on his head, went off without looking back.

The sun sank behind an ancient barrow for the night. The spring shadows hurriedly wrapped themselves over the steppe. The tractor driver climbed out of his seat and wiped the whitish dust off his cheek with his sleeve.

'Time for supper! Go home, Arseny Andreevich. The women will have milked the cows by now, and you can bring me out some warm milk.'

Arseny walked across the low growth of winter corn towards the village. As he started climbing the rise to the hilltop he heard the creak of a cart, and a woman's tearful voice:

'Gee up, damn you! What am I to do with you, you unclean spirits? Gee up!'

At the roadside, in a patch of loam wet with the evening dew, oxen harnessed into a cart were standing. Their sweaty backs were steaming. A little woman was dancing round them, waving a knout helplessly.

Arseny walked up to her and called:

'Good health, my girl!'

'Praise be, Arseny Andreevich.'

A hot wave of pleasure swept over Arseny, his knees trembled.

'Surely it isn't you, Anna?'

'Of course it's me, who else? I'm worn out with these oxen, they simply won't move. They're only a misery.'

'Where've you come from?'

'The mill. They loaded me with rye, and the oxen simply can't haul it.'

In a moment Arseny had slipped the coat off his shoulders and had flung it over the woman's arm, saying with a laugh:

'If I help to get you moving, will there be any reward?' He tried to look into her eyes.

But she turned her eyes away, and drew her kerchief down over them.

'Help me, for Christ's sake! We'll settle the account. . . .'

Arseny was twenty-seven, and he was strong. He carried six sacks up the hill, and then, sweating, went back down the slope. He seated himself on the cart to recover his breath.

'Well, how's things?' he asked. 'No news of your husband yet?'

'Cossacks who've come back from overseas, men who were with Wrangel, say he died in Turetchina.'

'And what do you propose to do?'

'Go on just the same. . . . Well, I must be moving, I'm already late. Thanks for the help, Arseny Andreevich.'

'You can't cut a greatcoat out of thanks.'

The smile faded on Arseny's lips; he was silent for a moment, then, bending over, with his left hand he gripped the head in the white kerchief, and pressed his lips to hers. They were trembling and cold, but his hand with its prickly callouses burnt her cheek shamefully, painfully. She tore herself away, and panted tearfully as she adjusted her kerchief:

'You filthy beast, you've got no shame whatever.'

'Why, what are you making a fuss about?' he asked, lowering his voice.

'Because I'm a married woman. It's disgraceful. You find some other woman if you want to behave like that.'

She tugged on the rein tied to the oxen's horns, and as she drove on to the road she shouted – but there were tears in her voice:

'You dogs all have only one idea. . . . Oh, gee up, damn you!'

The orchards bloomed with pink and white, heavily scented blossoms. In last year's sedges and by the slippery, rusty fallen trunks, which gave off a fermenting smell at night, in the Kachalovka pond, the frogs croaked their rounds, the geese hissed their love hisses, the mist rose from the water. . . . And the days were pleasant; Arseny, the chairman of the Kachalovka collective farm, felt a sunny joy in his heart, because the earth would no longer live its empty, bachelor existence: they had a tractor now. But his heart was troubled too: life meant little to him. For the third day running he had been up before the first cock, had gone out to the windmill in the steppe and seated himself beside the creaking tie-bar. Let the women pass judgement on him on the morrow, let the lads of the collective farm wink at him spitefully and laugh behind his back and to his face, if only he could see her, could tell her what he had felt ever since the autumn, when, during the threshing, he and she had piled the dark-brown oats on the rick with pitchforks: that labour and everything else in the world brought him no pleasure.

In the distance he perceived the white kerchief.

'Hallo, Anna Sergeevna.'

'Hallo, Arseny Andreevich.'

'I want to say a few words to you.'

She turned away, angrily crumpling her apron.

'Haven't you any conscience in front of people? What sort of talk can we have in the open field? . . . In front of all the women too! It's shameful.'

'But let me say it, all the same.'

'I've no time. The cow will go wandering into the maize.'

'Wait! I ask you to come to the alders at twilight; it's a business matter. . . .'

She drew her head down between her shoulders and walked off without looking back.

The alders stand locked in inseparable embraces; the exuberant bramble tendrils fetter the legs; the quails gather around the alders at night, and the mist unravels in curly streaks over the grass. Arseny waited there till darkness fell. When he heard a faint sh-sh of earth crumbling under someone's stealthy feet he felt his fingers go cold, and a sticky sweat moistened his brow.

'Did I upset you when I spoke to you today? Don't be angry, Anna.'

'I've grown used to that sort of thing now my husband's not around.'

'Well, but I want to say something quite serious. . . . You're living as a widow, your father-in-law doesn't need you. . . . Would you be willing to take me for husband? I'll look after you. . . . Now what's the matter, you queer creature? What are you snivelling for? It's nothing but trouble with you women. If you're doubtful because of your husband, if he does turn up I shan't try to force you to stay. . . . You can go back to him if you want to. . . .'

She sat down beside him on the damp, dewy ground. She

93

sat with head lowered. She drew invisible patterns in the earth with a dried stalk of steppe weed.

Arseny put his arms round her shyly; he was afraid she would tear herself away, would cry out, would call him names, as she had in the steppe. But when he glanced into her eyes, under the dark shadow of her kerchief he saw the traces of undried tears, and a smile.

'Anna, let them say what they like. . . . We'll go and sign up together, and you join the collective farm, work with us. How long do you intend to go on living this wretched life?'

Drought. Startling the cuckoos, the scythes ring and ring to one another through the orchards. If the people didn't mow the grass it would be gnawed from the roots. Beyond the Avdiushkin ravine the collective farm tractor was hauling two mowing machines. The day was dusty. And hot. Stooks of hay stuck up all over the steppe. The sun indicated that it was dinner-time: Arseny flung down his pitchfork, shook the prickly dust out of his shirt and went off to the steppe camp to have a wash. He saw his wife, Anna, coming to meet him; he recognized her nearly a mile away by her swift, swinging stride. She was bringing out food to the mowers. She came up to him, a flush on her sunburnt cheeks.

'Feeling tired, Anna? Why, it's a good ten miles to home.'

'No, not much. It would be easy going if it wasn't for the heat.'

They sat under a rick together; Arseny stroked her hand with his own, calloused through using the pitchfork, and heartened her with a smile.

But that evening she met him on the verandah; she was clinging firmly to the balustrade, as though she were afraid of falling. She had difficulty in getting the words out through her white lips:

'Arseny, my dear. . . . My husband. . . . Alexander's sent me a letter from Turetchina. . . . He promises to come home.'

To some, happiness in full; to others, only a scrap.

The grain of the Kachalovka individual farmers was burnt to the last ear; over the baked brown fields no virgin voice was to be heard; and to tell the truth, the corn had not even

94

come to fruition in the ear, there were only dry stalks, stunted and empty, ringing with emptiness in the wind. But on the collective farm, on the wedge of land between the Kachalovka and Ataman forests, along the high-road where all year the wind had scoffed at the pine board bearing the inscription 'Demonstration area', the Kuban wheat swayed to the height of a horse's belly. Who can ever say how things will turn out! At first, in the spring when the rain was falling on the Kachalovka fields, and the collective farm grain was only just beginning to sprout, the rich Kachalovka peasant Yashchurov (he owned twelve pairs of oxen, a drove of horses, a steam thresher, and he had grasping, mousy eyes) had said with a smirk, biting the end of his rye-coloured beard with his strong yellow teeth:

'God, ah, He sees the truth. . . . It's those who attend His services and read the Truth of Christ who get the rain, that's how it is. But it's washed up the collective Communists well and truly. Much too fast! As they say, you can't get far without God.'

And he said much else, and as he rode along the highway past the Kachalovka forest he halted his smooth dappled gelding and, pointing with his knout at the board swinging on the stake before the wind, he laughed, baring his boar's tusks. And his belly shook with his laughter:

'Demonstration area! The autumn will show that!'

The tractor broke up the ploughland to knee depth, but the Kachalovka individual peasants[1] pecked at the soil as best they could, in the manner of their grandfathers. The Kachalovka men scraped together an average of eight measures per *desyatin*, the collective gathered an average of forty measures. The Kachalovka men laughed, suppressing their envy:

'At any rate the orphans won't be neglected. . . .'

But one Sunday in September the Kachalovka individual peasants held a village meeting, and then went along to the collective farm yard. They stood arguing noisily around the granaries, which were bursting with grain; they hung around the tractor, grunting as they examined it and pawed it with their horny hands. And it was not until they were about to

[1] 'Individual peasant' is almost a technical term meaning a peasant who works on his own rather than in co-operation with other peasants.

95

leave that old Artiom, a real peasant farmer, called Arseny to one side and mumbled, thrusting his tobacco-stained beard into the chairman's ear:

'We've got a little request, Arseny Andreevich. Do us the godly favour, take us all together into your collective. There are twenty families of us, all poor.'

Arseny bowed joyfully to the old men:

'Glad to welcome you. . . .'

Now the collective farmers were up to their eyes in work. It was a year of drought. There was a shortage of grain in the neighbouring hamlets and villages. Beggars came in droves along the high-road past the Kachalovka forest. They turned aside into Kachalovka too; feeble, moaning voices grated outside the decorated shutters of the huts:

'For Christ's sake . . .'

A fly-blown window would be flung open, a bearded head would look out into the sun-baked street, and the owner would bark:

'Go in peace, strangers, or I'll set the dogs on you. There's the collective, go and ask them. They've set up the government here, and they ought to feed you.'

Every day the beggars dragged along in ones and twos and in flocks to the planed, resinous gates of the collective farm.

Arseny, his sunburnt cheeks sunken, waved his hands in despair:

'What can I do for you? We're full up everywhere. We shan't be able to feed ourselves and you too.'

But the collective farm women buzzed around Arseny with an anxious hum, like a swarm of bees, and the usual result was that Arseny and the men, waving the women off, went to the threshing floor, while the women led the strangers into a long barn fitted up as living-quarters. And all day the rattle of pots and the jangling of utensils could be heard through the windows of the spacious kitchen.

Occasionally the scalesman, old Artiom, would hurry panting to the threshing floor and, spitting with disgust, would cry hoarsely:

'There's no handling those women. . . . Get some order into them, Arseny. They've brought in a bunch of old men and taken the store keys from me. They're cooking dinner for them, they've taken wheat for another eight mouths.'

'You must manage with them somehow, old fellow,' Arseny smiled.

The membership of the collective farm was doubled. And the children also increased in number. While some of the workers were finishing the threshing or ploughing with teams of horses, others were building a school.

From first thing in the morning till it was quite dark at night the collective yard swarmed like an ant hill.

A machine rattled away in a shed. An electric lamp flooded the cleanly swept yard with waves of yellow light, and the horned moon hanging above Kachalovka was dimmed: it seemed greenish, small and unnecessary.

For two weeks Anna had been taking her turn at working in the cattle yard. With six other women she milked the cows, separated the calves and then went to bed. Sleep was slow in coming; she tossed and turned, listening to Arseny's regular breathing, thinking of the past and of her own present life in the collective farm.

All day the sky had been covered with a dense shroud of grey-blue clouds. From time to time there was a peal of thunder. The rooks were chattering in the orchard, the osiers were rustling; around the house a heavy scent rose from the flowering weeds by the fencing, and the spiny leaves of the nettles drooped to the ground. Beyond the shed lightning jumped like a lizard, thunder rolled, rain pattered over the roof, the wind sent little columns of dust whirling round the yard, a shutter caught by the wind banged to and fro, and the violent July downpour danced over the puddles, raising bubbles of foam.

Flinging her kerchief over her head, Anna ran out into the yard to take in the drying linen. The wet wind swept across the yard and lashed her face. As she ran to the granary, suddenly right above her thunder cracked hollowly, then rolled and rumbled away to die out somewhere beyond Kachalovka. Anna crouched down in alarm, crossed herself and whispered a prayer out of habit. When she stood up and looked back, by the

97

open gates she saw a cart and a man in a raincoat. The man was laughing, leaning backwards and baring his white teeth. Through the wind he shouted to Anna:

'What's the matter, my girl? Were you afraid of the prophet Elias?'[1]

Anna tucked up her skirt; as she took down the linen she shouted back angrily:

'You've no need to display your teeth for sale. No one here's going to buy them.'

Slipping as he came, the man in the raincoat walked up to her and said with a sarcastic smile:

'You're a bad-tempered lot, I can see that; but you've got no cause to be angry. D'you think you can save yourself from lightning by crossing yourself? And you're living in a collective farm!' he said reproachfully, again baring his teeth in a sarcastic smile.

That insulting smile seemed to burn Anna. For some reason she felt ashamed. Her answer sounded like an apology:

'I've not been living here long. . . .'

'Then it's not so bad.' The man went up the steps to the verandah, taking off his cap and waving it.

Anna finished taking down the linen and hurried back to the hut. When she entered the room she found the stranger in the raincoat sitting with Arseny. Her husband said to her:

'A teacher has arrived from the town. He'll teach all the people who're illiterate.'

The teacher looked at her with bright smiling eyes. She again felt a shameful awkwardness, and she went out as soon as she had put down the basket.

That evening, before they started supper, Arseny told her:

'After dinner tomorrow, you go and learn your letters. I've put your name down. We've got twenty illiterates altogether. You'll he having your lessons in the club.'

'I'm too ashamed, Arseny dear. . . . I'm not all that young.'

'It's more shameful to be illiterate.'

So next day Anna went to the club. The long table was crowded with pupils. Old Artiom was sitting with gaping

[1] The prophet Elijah, whose day is July 20th, is traditionally associated with thunderstorms, prevalent in that month. Tr.

mouth and sweating forehead. Auntie Daria had laid aside her knitting and was listening like the rest.

The teacher was saying something, as he drew a healthy-looking letter on the school blackboard.

When the door creaked everybody looked round, then bent over the table again. Anna went quietly across to the window and sat on the very edge of the bench. At first everything was strange, and she hid her smile from the others; but next day she listened more attentively, and boldly wrote a cramped and crooked letter 'B' on her sheet of paper.

She was drawn more and more to the club; she hurried over her dinner and almost ran along the corridor, a spelling book under her arm. It began to grow more cramped around the table. Fresh pupils turned up. Old Artiom swore under his breath and thrust out his elbows, pushing Auntie Daria right to the edge of the bench. From dinner-time till dusk the club was alive with whispering and the restrained hum of voices.

A spacious room with six windows had been taken over for the club. A table covered with red cloth stood by one wall, and there were portraits and banners in a corner.

In the end old Artiom pushed Auntie Daria right off the bench; she shifted from the table to the window ledge. It was hot in the room, the sun peered inquisitively through the windows. A glittering fly buzzed and beat against the glass. In the room there was silence. Old Artiom sucked his scrap of pencil, and pursed his lips as he wrote. The air was heavy with the smell of home-grown tobacco and onion. The people on each side of Anna squeezed against her and jogged her. The woman next to her, Martha, had four small children; but she knew they were being looked after in the crèche, so her eyes calmly followed the letters. The sweat dripped in little beads from her nose on to her upper lip; she brushed them away with her sleeve and waved off the importunate flies, while her lips formed the words.

Anna's heart beat faster. Today she was to read a whole word for the first time. She wrote one letter, then a second, a third and a word appeared out of what formerly had been an incomprehensible jumble to her. She nudged her neighbour:

'Look! I've made the word "farmworker".'

The teacher tapped the blackboard with his chalk:

'Quiet! Read to yourselves. Now, daddy Artiom, read today's lesson to us.'

With his two palms the old man pressed the spelling book firmly against the table, and cleared his throat:

'O-u-r f-l-o-u-r.'

Martha couldn't restrain her laughter; she snorted into her hand. The old man gave her an angry side-glance, and began again:

'Ou-r flo-ur is goo-od.' Then he flung out his hands in despair. 'Tell me, for mercy's sake, what does that sound like?' As he turned over the page he whispered to Martha: 'No, my dear woman, I'm growing old. When I was young I could thresh three lots of wheat without stopping, with never a puff into my whiskers. But now, you see how it is, I'm worn out only with reading. I'm as broken-winded as if I'd hauled a cart uphill.'

Anna was enjoying her work, either in the kitchen or with the cattle. The threshing machine clattered away on the threshing floor, the workers hurried around busily. Arseny, spattered with grain awns and dust, was building the rick; but at noon he ran to the kitchen and called to Anna:

'You're one of the stronger girls, Anna; go and give a hand on the threshing floor, and let Martha Ignatovna take over from you.'

As he helped Anna to climb on to the rick, he slapped her on the back and laughed:

'Now, my buxom wench, be quick on the receiving end!' He raised a great load of scented, threshed straw on his pitchfork and, tensing his body, lifted it up to her. She took it over. He piled the straw round her, first to her knees, then to her waist; laughing as he gazed up at her, he shouted:

'Hey, you there up on the rick! Going to sleep? You're holding up the work!'

Now she had regular work to do, Anna's sorrow was swallowed up and lost in the past. She stopped wondering what would happen if her first husband were to return. The summer slipped by like brief summer lightning. . . . Autumn settled in around the collective farm gates. The children ran off to school each morning, kicking up their heels as though they were a drove of foals turned loose.

But then, one frosty and gossamer-threaded autumn day, Anna's husband Alexander walked on to the verandah in the early morning, keeping off the dog with a hazel switch. His heels clattering harshly, he walked along the verandah, opened the door and halted at the threshold, uttering not a word of greeting. He just stood there, tall, swarthy, in a shabby military greatcoat, and said simply, curtly:

'I've come for you, Anna. Get yourself ready.'

Anna ran to and fro from the chest to the bed, with numb fingers snatching up first one article then another. She pulled down her winter shawl from the clothes rail, then squatted down heavily, her eyes shifting from Arseny to her husband. Hardly able to open her lips, she said:

'I'm not coming.'

'You're not coming? . . . We'll see about that!' Alexander smiled wrily, shrugged his shoulders and went out, closing the door behind him carefully and firmly.

During that long and changeable autumn Anna was often unwell; her face turned sallow, with illness or maybe with thought. One Saturday evening she and the other women milked the cows and separated the calves, driving them into the byre. Anna counted one short, and went off to look for it, going through the orchards into the steppe, past the windmill dozing in the haze. She found the dappled calf grazing in an ancient abandoned cemetery, among the moss-grown crosses and musty, settled graves. Straining her eyes in the gathering darkness, she drove the calf home. When she reached a ditch she had to sit down, pressing her hands to her breast. She heard her heart beating, and then a knocking and fidgeting. She rose heavily and went on, smiling wearily and expectantly with the corners of her lips.

The orchard was bare; the wind was tossing under the crowns of the poplars, strewing leaves like scraps of red material thinly underfoot. When she reached the summer-house she saw someone emerge from the thorns and stand barring her path.

'Is that you, Anna?'

She recognized Alexander by the voice. He came up to her, stooping a little, his arms wide open.

'So you've forgotten how we lived together six years? . . . So you've lost all conscience while you've been a soldier's grass widow? Ah, you loose woman!'

Anna was thinking: 'Now he'll knock me down, he'll kick me with his iron-shod soldier's boots, just as he used to when we lived together.' But unexpectedly Alexander went down on his knees in the damp smelly mud, and said huskily, stretching his hands out to her:

'Anna, dearest, have pity! Didn't I love you? Didn't I look after you as if you were a little child? D'you remember how sometimes I used a filthy word to my mother because she started swearing at you? Or have you forgotten our love? I came back from abroad with only one thought in my head: to see you. . . . But you . . . ah . . .'

He scrambled up heavily, rose to his feet and went off through the thorn bushes without looking back. At a turn he glanced back and shouted hoarsely:

'But mark my words: If you don't come back to me, if you don't give that lover of yours the chuck, I'll do some mischief.'

Anna remained standing there. Inside her, pity, like a snake, was warming towards him, towards the man with whom she had lived six years under one roof. . . . That evening marked the turn. She was more and more sunk in thought, recalling the past; she refused to quicken the memory of their days of quarrelling, when her husband had beaten her almost to death, and remembered only the bright joyous days. And her heart swelled with warmth for the past and for Alexander, while Arseny's image faded into a haze, fell into the background.

Arseny could not recognize his former Anna: she grew unsociable with him; bending slightly backwards with her swollen belly, she walked silently about the room; she avoided the other women on the farm, and Arseny more and more frequently caught her gaze, hateful and bitter, resting on him.

One midnight, in the threshing floor out on the steppe, not far from the Avdiushkin ravine, three ricks of collective-farm hay were burnt down. Shortly after the first cock Mitrokh the cobbler, dressed only in his pants, came running to Arseny and rattled at the frost-patterned window:

'Get up! The hay's on fire. . . . Arson!'

Not stopping to dress, Arseny hurried out to the verandah, gazed through the latticing of the cherry trees into the steppe, and swore violently between his clenched teeth. Beyond the rise, above the sheeting of white snow, a lurid column was rising right up to the moon, flickering in the wind. Old Artiom led a mare out of the stable, bridled her, flung himself belly downwards across her bony back, with a grunt threw one leg over her and trotted off to the fire. As he rode past the verandah he shouted to Arseny:

'Someone's done this out of spite. My poor little skewbald! My mare. . . . She'll die of hunger now. We'll be tying their tails one to another and driving them out of the yard!'

When dawn came Arseny went out to the scene of the fire. Around the heaps of smoking ash the bare earth was steaming; little green shoots were gazing up trustfully.

He squatted down on his heels and looked about him. On the sweating ground and in the half-melted snow were traces of British iron-shod boots; the tiny holes stamped out by the nail-heads were like black pock-marks. He lit a cigarette and, keeping a close eye on the tracks that ran in tangled skeins across the steppe, made his way back to Kachalovka. The tracks tied into loops and were lost; a little farther on the wearer of the boots had scraped away the fine ice above the ravine as his feet slipped. And Arseny followed the human tracks confidently, silently, as though they were an animal's. Close to the nearest threshing floor, by Alexander's fence, he lost them. He grunted, flung his old fowling-piece – a legacy from his father – from one shoulder to the other and went off along the road to the collective farm.

The midwife gave the slippery little body a slap and called over the partition as she washed her hands in a bowl:

'Listen, Arseny: a commune baby's been born. I suppose you won't have him christened?'

103

Arseny silently drew aside the cloth curtain; from under the blood-stained blanket Anna's ashen face gazed at him with hateful eyes, and as she swallowed back her tears she hissed:

'Go away! I don't love you. I wish I'd never set eyes on you.'

She turned herself to the wall and burst into tears.

Her life had been running smoothly, like a high-road of beaten earth. But now a salty lump went cold in her throat, and grief leapt into her heart with a wolfish spring.

Some two days later Arseny went to the shed to finish threshing the last of the millet. He was busy with the engine till dark; by the time they had finished dusk was falling, and night was lurking beyond the dark crowns of the poplars. He heard a voice:

'Arseny Andreevich, come outside for a moment.'

He went out. By the boarded wall Anna was standing, wrapped in a shawl.

'What do you want, Anna?'

The strange hoarse voice that answered him did not sound like his wife's:

'I ask you, for God's sake . . . let me go to my husband. He's calling me. . . . He says he'll take me and the child. . . . Arseny Andreevich, don't hold it against me, and don't keep me back! I'll leave you all the same; you don't love me any more.'

'First feed the child till it's weaned, and then go; I won't force you. . . . But I shan't let you have my son. I fought four years for the Soviets, I got several wounds. But your husband was a White, he came back from Wrangel. . . . If he brings up my boy he'll make him slave for him. And I don't want that.'

She went right up to him and breathed hotly into his face:

'You won't let me have the child?'

'No!'

'You won't?'

Arseny's heart boiled with fury; for the first time in all the months of his life together with Anna he clenched his fist and was about to hit her between those eyes which were burning with hatred for him. But he controlled himself, and said thickly:

'You watch out, Anna!'

After supper that evening Anna fed the child at her breast, and then, throwing a kerchief over her head, went out into the yard. She did not return for a long time. Arseny was bent over the bench, fashioning a horse collar. He heard the door creak. He recognized her by her step, without turning his head. She went to the cradle, changed the napkin and went to bed without saying a word. Arseny, too, lay down. He could not sleep; he tossed about, listening to his wife's broken breathing and the uneven beating of his own heart. Around midnight he dozed off. Sleep took possession of him. He did not hear Anna slip off the bed as quietly as a cat, just after the first cock. She dressed without lighting the lamp, wrapped the child in a shawl and went out without making the door creak.

Anna had lived with Alexander for over a month. At first she had experienced a tremulous happiness, and only rarely did her secret tears express her regret for the pleasant life of the collective farm. But then her father-in-law began grumbling spitefully:

'You've brought a loose hussy into the home. . . . There wasn't any stink of communal life in our hut. You've taken in a brazen, lazy slut. You should keep her hard at it!'

During the first few days Alexander treated her kindly; but those days brightened with kindness were followed by a black succession of days of labour beyond her strength. Her husband piled the farm work on to her, while he himself took to going more and more frequently to the outskirts of the village, to Lushka, the distiller of illicit vodka. He would come home drunk and decorate the walls and the floor with vomit. Then he would sit sprawled on the bench till dawn came, his fur cap thrust back on his nape, belching the stink of home-distilled vodka and self-satisfiedly twisting his whiskers..

'What are you really, Anna? You're nothing but illiteracy, ignorance. Now we, we've seen the world, we've been abroad and we know superior manners. Really, why did I have to take a woman like you for wife? Pardon! Any general's daughter would have fallen for me. Sometimes in the officers' . . . but what's the point of telling you: all the same you wouldn't understand. . . . The Red swine should spend some time abroad, that's where you find real people.'

He dropped off to sleep where he sat on the bench. When he woke up in the morning he roared hoarsely:

'Wife! Take my boots off. You good-for-nothing, you should show respect to me for feeding you and your whelp. What are you snivelling for? Asking for a taste of the whip? Watch out, or you'll get it, and soon!'

One melting, cloudy February day the village policeman knocked on the little window of Alexander's hut:

'Are the masters at home?'

'Come in; we're all at home.'

He came in, put his stick, well marked with dog's teeth, down on the chest, took out a greasy sheet of paper from his breast pocket and spread it out carefully on the table.

'You're to go to the village meeting at once. With the likes of us it can't be otherwise, I'm chasing everybody and making them sign. Sign your names.'

Anna went to the table and signed the sheet. Her husband raised his eyebrows in astonishment:

'Where did you learn to write?'

'In the collective farm.'

Alexander said no more; he closed the door behind the departing policeman, and then said sternly:

'I shall go and listen to their Soviet stupidities, but you see to the cattle, Anna. And don't give them the millet straw; if I see you have I'll give you something to remember me by. You've begun to make a habit of it. . . . We've got two months of winter still, but you've used up half the store.'

Breathing heavily, he buttoned up his sheepskin jerkin, and looked at her from under his shaggy eyebrows with a miserly stare. Anna hesitated a moment by the stove, then she sidled up to her husband:

'Alick . . . Perhaps I could go . . . to the meeting with you.'

'To where?'

'To the meeting.'

'What for?'

'To listen.'

A heavy flush spread slowly over Alexander's cheeks, the corners of his lips began to quiver and his right hand went out to the wall and felt for the whip hanging above the bed.

'What d'you want to do, you straying bitch: bring shame on your husband in the eyes of all the village? When will you get your Communist tricks out of your head?' Grating his teeth and clenching his fists, he stepped over to her. 'You're only a . . . a . . . I'll show you, damn and blast you! Not another word from you!'

'But Alick, dear, the women do go to meetings. . . .'

'Shut your mouth, you bitch! Don't try to force your habits on me! The women who go to meetings are the ones without husbands, the women who go wagging their tails in the wind. A fine idea! You go to the meeting!'

The insult stung Anna as if it had been a needle. She turned pale, and said in a hoarse, quivering voice:

'So you don't regard me as a human being?'

'A mare's not a horse, a woman's not a human being.'

'But in the collective . . .'

'You and your bastard are not guzzling collective food but mine. It's my neck you're sitting on, it's me you'll listen to!' he roared.

But Anna, feeling her cheeks turning pale and the blood rushing to her heart, flooding her veins with heat, said through her clenched teeth:

'You yourself persuaded me, you promised to have pity on me. But where are your promises now?'

'This is where!' he shouted, giving her a swinging blow on the breast with his fist.

She staggered back, cried out and tried to seize her husband's hand. But he grasped her by the hair, swearing hoarsely, and kicked her violently in the belly. She fell heavily to the floor, gasping for air with her gaping mouth, panting with a burning, choking feeling. And now she accepted the dull pain of his kicks with indifference, seeing his livid, contorted face above her as though through a fine film of mist.

'Take that! Take that, you . . . You don't like it? Ah, you filthy bitch! You'll dance to a different tune with me! Take that . . . and that!'

Every blow he aimed at his wife's motionless, huddled body only increased his fury; he beat her measuredly, aiming his kicks at her belly, her breast, her face, which she was covering with her hands. He kicked her until his shirt was wet with sweat and his legs were tired. Then he put on his fur cap, spat and went into the yard, slamming the door behind him.

Out in the street he halted at the gate, stood thinking for a moment, then wandered off through the decrepit fences of his neighbour's yard to Lushka the illicit distiller.

Anna lay on the floor until evening. As dusk was falling her father-in-law came into the room and, stirring her with the toe of his boot, stormed at her:

'You, get up! We know how good you are at pretending! Your husband hardly touches you with his finger, and you stretch yourself out like that! Run to the Soviets and complain. . . . Get up, will you? Who's going to see to the cattle if you don't? Or would you like us to hire a labourer?' He went into the kitchen, shuffling his feet over the earthen floor. 'She can manage to eat enough for four! But work . . .? Ah, the conscience of some people! Spit in her eyes and she'd say it's God's dew.'

He dressed and went out to see to the cattle. Anna's infant started fidgeting, it began to cry in the cradle. She came round, crawled to her knees, spat out the sand mixed with blood and spittle through her broken lips and muttered, with difficulty opening her mouth:

'My poor little one. . . .'

Beyond Kachalovka, on the slope embroidered with thawing patches of snow, the evening was met by the night. Over the crumbling, spongy drifts the hares scampered into the village to take a look around. A few little yellow dots of light shone out in Kachalovka. The wind spread the heavy scent of burning dung bricks along the street.

Alexander arrived home just before supper-time. He fell on to the bed, and grunted:

'Anna! My boots! . . .' Then he dropped off to sleep, snoring and wetting the pillow with his sticky dribble.

Anna waited until her father-in-law was busy at the stove, then she snatched up the child and ran out. She stood for a moment, listening to the rapid beating of her heart. Night was striding over Kachalovka. Water was dripping from the roofs, the dung stacked in heaps was steaming. The snow underfoot was raw and clinging. Pressing the child to her breast, stumbling along, she walked by the side road to the Kachalovka pond; it showed blue before her with the dirty azure of its ice. Around the pond the uncut sedges were creaking in the wind and haughtily nodding their shaggy heads at her.

She went up to the ice-hole. The black water was filmed with thin fresh ice; around the hole shards of ice and frozen cattle dung had been swept into heaps.

Pressing the child more tightly to her breast, she looked into the black, gaping maw of the hole, and went down on her knees. But suddenly – unexpectedly – muffled under the napkins and blanket – the infant started crying. Shame swept over Anna in a hot wave. She jumped up, and started running; she ran all the way to the collective farm without looking back. There they stood, the smoothly planed gates yellowed by the winter; she heard the familiar, homely roar of the dynamo running in the shed.

Staggering as she went, she ran along the verandah; the door leading to the passage creaked, her heart beat heavily in time with the tramp of her feet. The third door on the left. She knocked. No answer. She knocked louder. Someone was coming to the door. It was opened. Anna looked with glazing eyes, saw Arseny, thin and yellow in the face, and leaned helplessly against the doorpost.

He carried her in his arms to the bed, undressed the child and laid it in the cradle, which had stood empty for two months. He ran to the kitchen for scalded milk and, kissing his son's swollen little feet and Anna's tear-stained face, said:

'That's just why I didn't come for you. . . . I knew you'd come back to the collective, and that you'd be coming back soon.'

1925

109

The Outrage

Trampling down the low growth of joyless corn, a hot burning wind blew over the steppe from the east. The sky was deathly dark, the grass caught fire, a grey dust swirled low along the high-roads; scorched by the sun, the earth's crust split and cracked. And the cracks, charcoaled and furrowed like the lips of a man dying of thirst, bled with the deep, salty smells of the soil.

Striding over the steppe from the Black Sea, the drought trod the grain with iron hoofs.

In the hamlet of Dubrovin the people lived only for the time of harvest. They waited and were worn out with hope, gazing at the glassy blue of the sky, at the prickly sun, which looked like a bearded ear of wheat in a spiky fringe of awns.

Their hopes were burnt up together with the grain. In August they started stripping the bark from the elms and the oaks; they ground and ate it, mixing a handful of millet flour with a troughful of oak dough.

Just before the Blessed Virgin's day Stepan, half dropping with exhaustion, drove the oxen out to his allocation of land, harnessed them to the plough and, baring his teeth in his pain, biting the edges of his chapped lips, silently took hold of the plough handles.

He ploughed eleven acres that week. The furrows turned out crooked and poor, shallow, with brown clumps of faulty ploughing, as though it was not shares that were carving through the grassy ploughland, but someone's feeble, twisted fingers.

Stepan went out to make his bow to the faithless soil because, in addition to his wife, he had a family of eight mouths, the children of his son who had been killed in the Civil War, while there was only himself, with fifty years hanging over his bowed back, to do the work. He ploughed his land and then sold his second pair of oxen. Or rather, he hardly sold them so much as gave them to a good man in exchange for ten hundredweight of unsifted grain.

But then, soon after the holy day, the chairman of the village Soviet announced:

'Seed grain is being handed out. When we're through the autumn a paper will come from the centre, and we'll be going to collect. If you haven't ploughed already, get down to it. Gnaw the ground with your teeth if necessary, but turn over the soil!'

'It's all a trick; they won't issue any seed,' the Cossacks declared.

'But we've got the notice. It's all as it should be, and no tricks about it.'

'They take it from us, but as for giving . . .' Stepan tormented himself with longing and hope. And he believed, and yet he didn't.

The autumn passed. The village was half buried in snow. Hares' tracks were visible in the deserted orchards.

'Well, are they issuing the seed?' Stepan pestered the chairman.

The chairman waved his hand spitefully:

'Don't keep on at me, Stepan Prokofich. We've not got any instructions yet.'

'And there won't be any. Don't expect them. The people's minds had to be turned from the thought of death . . . so they raised our hopes. . . . They threw us hope like a bone to a dog.' Stepan shook his horny fists savagely. 'Damn them, the sons of bitches! They're eating plenty of bread in the towns, blast them. . . .'

'Don't say too much, Stepan Prokofich. I'll have you inside for that.'

'Bah!' Stepan waved him off and, without saying all he felt like, he carried his big bony body out of the Soviet office. He was like a sick bullock: his angular shoulder blades stuck out under his patched jerkin, his ragged striped trousers flapped round his withered knees. A greenish sediment was sprinkled over his red beard. He looked sidelong with a hungry, savage glance, and felt ashamed of his incommensurably huge frame, now shrunken to a stick. He went home and dropped on to the bench.

'See to the cattle! Lying there, you marmot!' his wife went for him.

'Varvara can see to them.'

'She hasn't got anything to go outside in.'

'She can wear my felt boots.'

Varvara, a teen-ager, drew off her grandfather's felt boots from his feet and went to tend the cattle, while he lay with his long bare feet sticking up, his eyelids flickering rapidly over his closed eyes. He sighed, groaned and thought dreary, joyless thoughts. But at dinner-time he seated himself at the head, and hung his bony carcass over the table as he surveyed his grandchildren. He noticed that the youngest of them, the three-year-old Timoshka, with an awkward smile on his face, was surreptitiously trying to catch a small piece of potato floating in the pot, and he gave him a ringing blow on his forehead with a spoon:

'Stop fishing!'

In the village people died off; through eating bread made from oak bark they were perforated like a tree with worms. And a gloomy longing disturbed Stepan at night: he had nothing with which to sow his ploughed land.

The price of cattle fell to nothing. For one cow people gave one hundred and eighty to two hundred and twenty pounds of rye, unsorted and full of weeds. At Yuletide there was again talk of seed being issued, but once more the rumour came to nothing. It died away like the southern wind in the steppe late in the autumn. It revived only as spring was on the way. One evening, at a meeting in the church vestry, the Soviet chairman announced:

'The paper's arrived.' He fingered his Adam's apple, and ended: 'We can drive for the grain tomorrow if you like. So you see, they don't forget us. . . .' He was so moved that he could not finish.

It was a hundred miles from the village to the district centre. The villagers were broken up into separate parties by their very first halt for the night. The men who had horses travelled more quickly, the oxen sledges extended in a long queue. Stepan had his neighbour Afonka, a muscular young Cossack, as his companion. Their road ran through the Tauride settlements. By nightfall they had covered only twenty to twenty-five miles. The oxen, emaciated with lack of fodder, moved slowly, meagrely measuring their steps, leaning their bony flanks against the centre-pole.

Stepan walked all the way, in order to spare his oxen's strength for the return journey. They drove off from their last night bivouac as soon as the moon rose, and reached the district centre late the next morning.

Around the elevator excited horses were fighting and squealing, oxen were bellowing, a large crowd contributed their share to the hubbub.

Late in the afternoon a dusty scalesman ran out of the elevator gate and shouted as he looked around the sledges:

'Dubrovin men, drive up! Where's your chairman?'

'Here!' the chairman barked as if he were on parade.

'Got your order?'

'Yes, we've got it.'

While the Cossacks who had arrived earlier were harnessing up again, Stepan and Afonka were able to work their way right to the gate. A big, swarthy Cossack in a cap of the Ataman regiment and a cowl flung back over his leather jerkin stood across their path, pleading with an ox which kept shaking its head:

'Steady now! Steady, you devil! Now, now, do stand still!'

'Move aside, friend,' Stepan asked him.

'You can drive round me, can't you?'

'Where can we drive round? We'd break our shafts.'

'Pull your sledge over to one side,' Afonka shouted. 'You're right across the road, like a snowdrift. Come on, have a heart!'

The Cossack gave his restive ox a hefty blow with his fist, and the animal, rolling its bloodshot eyes, thrust its furrowed neck into the yoke.

'Come on now, drive up!' the scalesman bawled, waving the order as he stood at the door of the delivery shed. Stepan put his oxen into a jog-trot, and was the first to reach the scales.

A golden, rustling flood of wheat flowed down the iron-shod

sleeve into his sack. Panting with the scented warm dust and his joy, he held the edges of the sack open and stared in amazement at the scalesman's unconcerned look as he indifferently crushed the spilt grain with his boots.

'That's the lot!' the man said. 'Seven hundred and fifty pounds.'

Straining his arms, Stepan tried to raise a heavy sack higher, as in former days, and unexpectedly felt his knees quivering uncontrollably; he staggered, took a couple of uncertain, hobbling steps and then had to lean against the door.

'Get on with you! Don't hang about!' the Cossacks crowding round the entrance urged him.

'He's worn out, poor old fellow!'

'His powder's got damp!'

'Hold on to the ground, or you'll fall!'

'Ho-ho-ho!'

'Drop your sack and I'll pick it up: it's just my size.'

The Cossack who had been harnessing his oxen at the gate helped Stepan to drag his sacks to the sledge, and when Afonka came back they drove off together into the square. Dusk was falling.

'Go and ask someone for a night's lodging,' Afonka, who was frozen with the cold, suggested.

'But why don't you go?'

'You've got a beard, Prokofich. You look more likely.'

Stepan walked along the street; but not one household was prepared to let him in:

'We have the likes of you calling every day.'

'Nowhere here. Full up!'

'Spend the night in the street.'

With difficulty opening his swollen lips, Stepan pleaded:

'Let us in! We can lie together. Haven't you any Christian feeling?'

'Today we live without Christians, we have tin-plate.'

'Go somewhere else, old man.' They waved him away.

He came out of the last yard, and harshly brought his knout down on one of his innocent oxen.

'A fine lot of people, Afonka! We'll have to spend the night under the fence, that's clear.'

'I'd set fire to their houses at all four corners. They're not human beings, they're wolves. They wouldn't give you snow in the middle of winter!'

They unharnessed their oxen on the elevator square, and lay down on top of the sacks in their sledges, listening to the roar of railway engines. The square was in continual uproar. Several young Cossacks, gathered round a sledge at the far end, were singing harmoniously. One of them sang, in a hoarse. but powerful voice:

> *'Youthful Cossacks went a-riding,*
> *From their service homeward.'*

Other voices, rough with the wind and frost, took up the refrain:

> *'On their shoulders epaulettes,*
> *On their chests were crosses. . . .'*

As he listened to the singing Stepan distrustfully groped for the tied necks of his tightly filled sacks, and his closed eyes brought him visions of his strip of black ploughed land, right by the Ataman tumulus; and he saw himself scattering the full-bodied seed in handfuls.

Around midnight a bitter wind began to blow from the north. The snow glittered like crystals on the roofs of the trucks arrived from Moscow; along the side of the track the earth, laid bare by a thaw, turned dark and smelt of the previous autumn, the first frosts, the freezing highway.

The elevator rose in a ghostly square block above the town. The oxen huddled dejectedly against the palisades of the fence; the wind blew a frosty dust over the square and was stranded on the telegraph wires, wailing thinly, piercingly.

Late in the night, when the handle of the Dipper was thrust down into the flat elevator roof, Stepan woke up. He shifted his stiff legs and got out of the sledge. The oxen, white with rime, were lying beside it, breathing heavily; the sledges showed up black, like overturned haycocks; homeless dogs were cowering around in the cold.

Stepan aroused Afonka, they harnessed up and drove out of the town in the thickening darkness before the dawn.

They climbed the hill. A railway engine wailed over the town. Afonka, striding along to Stepan's side, waved his knout back at the houses behind them:

'The way it bellows, the damned stallion! It drags hundreds of tons behind it and need hardly even grunt. But we've been loaded with only seven hundred pounds and we've got to foot it all the way back. At any rate you've got oxen; but look at that one of mine on the right: a three-year-old, and a cow to make things worse. Give her the knout, and the beast turns up her tail and tries to squirt muck over you. Get on, you fancy young lady!' Rolling his yellow, swollen, rheumy eyes, he swung his knout violently at the cow and fell over into the sledge with his legs sticking up in the air.

By noon they had reached the village of Olkha Roga. People dressed in their holiday clothes thronged the streets. Only then did Stepan remember that the day was Sunday. They drove up to the church and stopped.

'We shan't be able to make that hill with our sledges. Look: the road's bare of snow,' Stepan said.

'Seems like it!' Afonka agreed. 'It's all sand, no snow at all.'

'We'll have to hire a light cart to carry the grain to the top.'

'You arrange it, and we'll pay with grain.'

On poles laid down outside a farmyard eight or nine Tauridans were having a Sunday afternoon doze, and husking sunflower seeds. Stepan went up to them and took off his shaggy fur cap:

'Good living to you, good people.'

'Good health to you,' answered the oldest, a man with a grizzled beard.

'Would one of you hire us a cart to take a load up the hill? The road here's nothing but sand and little snow, and we've got sledges. . . .'

'Hm!' the Tauridan answered curtly, sprinkling his beard with husks.

'We'll pay. Help us, for Christ's sake.'

'We haven't any horses.'

116

'But, good people, are we to be stuck here?' Stepan pleaded with an imploring gesture.

'That we can't say,' another man, in a triangular hareskin cap, answered unconcernedly.

For a moment there was a silence among them. Afonka came up, and made a low bow:

'Do us this kindness.'

'We can't. You'll have to drive your animals a little harder.'

A stalwart, young Tauridan in a good-quality leather jerkin came over to Stepan and clapped him on the shoulder:

'I tell you what, daddy; you and me will have a fight. If you beat me I'll carry you up the hill; but if you don't, I won't. Well, what do you say?' His round grey eyes smiled in the oily flush of his cheeks.

Stepan looked the smiling Tauridan up and down and put on his cap.

'So you think you can make fun of us, brothers? It's clear you're not bothered by other people's troubles.'

'Let's try!' the young Tauridan laughed, raising and lowering his eyebrows playfully under his lamb-skin cap.

Stepan pulled off his gloves and stood examining the broad shoulders of his opponent, who had taken off his jerkin.

'Ready?' asked Stepan.

'Now that sounds like business!' said the Tauridan.

They clutched each other round the waist. Thrusting his fingers under Stepan's red girdle, breathing merrily and easily, the Tauridan asked:

'Tuck in your tummy!'

They circled round slowly, testing each other's strength.

Narrowing his eyes, Stepan thrust his shoulders forward, pressing it against his opponent's chest. The Tauridan drew one leg right back and pulled Stepan over against himself, trying to break his resistance. They circled round three times. Stepan felt that the young, well-fed Tauridan was stronger than he, and though he went on with the struggle he was gloomily certain of its outcome.

Evidently he had to act quickly: he bent his left knee and flung himself down, striking his head painfully on a frozen clod. Tripped by Stepan's legs, the Tauridan flew over him and fell heavily. Stepan tried to leap up youthfully, as in former days; but his legs refused to answer his will, and the Tauridan was already back on his feet and on top of him, pressing his shoulders into the snow pitted by horses' hoofs.

The other Tauridans stood around them, roaring with laughter, slapping their gloved hands together. Stepan sighed as he beat the mud out of his cap:

'If I'd been ten years younger I'd have shown you. . . .'

'All right, daddy, I'll carry you to the top of the hill. You've earned it,' the young Tauridan said, panting, and smiling with self-satisfaction. 'Drive over to that yard.'

They loaded the grain on to a large cart, and the Tauridan who had wrestled with Stepan cracked his elegant knout over his three well-fed horses, saying to Stepan and Afonka:

'You follow behind.'

At the top, some three miles from the settlement, they transferred the grain back to the sledges. Here the road was under deeply rutted snow.

The oxen were exhausted with the heavy going. The gleaming sledge runners left tracks on the frozen ground, and it looked as though it had been swept by women's skirts.

There were still twenty miles between them and their village. Stepan suggested:

'Let's keep going, Afonka. We'll get there tonight, even if it is dark.'

'There's nothing to stop for, we haven't a scrap of fodder. It would only tire the oxen even more.'

By nightfall they reached the Government forest. A plentiful shower of stars glittered drily, hazily, in the clear black sky. The night was frosty. Stepan was driving in front. They dropped down into a valley. Ahead of his oxen a slanting shadow fell across the road, a man emerged from the darkness.

'Who's that coming?' the stranger asked.

'We're Dubrovin men returning from the district centre,' Stepan said warily, looking back at Afonka.

'Halt!'

'Who says we should?'

'Halt, I tell you. . . .'

The man, who was stocky and had his face half concealed in a cowl, came up to Stepan. In his hand gleamed the chilly barrel of a pistol.

'What are you carrying?' he demanded.

'Seed grain. . . .' Stepan's heart quivered, his voice quivered. He looked to one side, and saw a cart drawn by four horses coming up alongside his sledge. The man in the cowl came right up to him and thrust the cold, sweaty steel barrel under his cap:

'Unload!'

'What's your game?' Stepan groaned, leaning weakly against his sledge.

'Unload, I tell you!'

Two men ran over from the cart, their boots squeaking in the snow.

'Shoot him!' one of them shouted as he ran. The pistol thrust under Stepan's fur cap cut into his temple. He slipped down on his knees.

'Unload!' the man in the cowl roared furiously, bending over him and pushing the pistol barrel against Stepan's teeth.

'It's seed grain. . . . Brothers. . . . My dear . . . brothers. . . . Oh!' Stepan sobbed, crawling on his knees to the man, cutting his hands on the frozen clods.

One of the two men who had come from the cart sent Afonka down with a blow from his rifle butt, and flung the tarpaulin from his sledge over him:

'Lie still, don't try to peep!'

The cart rattled up and stopped by the sledges. Two of the men heaved the sacks of grain into it, grunting under the weight; the third, the one wearing the cowl, stood over Stepan. Under his drooping, straggling whiskers he bared his rimed, toothy mouth.

'Take your tarpaulin,' ordered a fourth man, sitting on the cart seat.

The oxen found the empty sledges easy to draw, and they set off along the road. Afonka went up to Stepan, who was still lying stretched out on the ground.

'Get up. They've gone. . . .'

The wheels of the retreating cart rattled dully over the virgin soil at the roadside. Swallowing the blood rising in his mouth, Stepan clambered to his feet. He could see the black outline of the cart disappearing in the distance. A moment or two later the crack of a single shot, evidently fired to frighten them, went rolling across the valley.

'What filthy luck!' Afonka said huskily and, breaking the knout in his hands, he cried out: 'It's an outrage!'

Dishevelled, a fearful sight, Stepan got up and circled round slowly in the bluish, icy light of the moon. Afonka stood with bowed shoulders, hunched up, and looked at him, recalling something he had seen the previous winter. He had shot a wolf in the orchard, and the animal, blinded by a sprinkle of grapeshot in its eyes, had circled round and round outside the threshing floor just as Stepan was doing now. Then it had sunk down in the crumbling snow, squatting on its hind legs, dying a dumb, voiceless death.

In the fourth week of Lent the whole village went out to the sowing.

Stepan sat by his verandah, drawing with a stick in the softened, sticky earth, frenziedly caressing the soil with his sunken eyes.

For a whole week he went about taciturn and grey of face. His family, who had wept and wailed on his return, had quietened down, and fearfully watched his shaking head, his helpless hands aimlessly fingering his ruddy beard. He made his first visit to the Ataman tumulus during the night of Passion Sunday. The steppe, fringed with silvery lunar embroidery, was steaming with mist. A leveret was rummaging wearily among the last-year scrub, and the old grass rustled stiffly, pressed upon by the young shoots of the fresh growth. A few low clouds dragged slowly over the sky, hiding the young moon, and the rays sifting through the cloudy sieve noiselessly fingered the feeble, drowsy grass. Some one hundred and fifty yards away from his plot of land Stepan came to a halt, and remained standing under the Ataman tumulus.

On the farther side of the mound extended the ploughed land which he had deceived. The shoots of young grass nestled in the furrows, a vigorous growth of bindweed entangled the upturned black earth. Stepan found it difficult to pass round the tumulus, to look at the black clods spread out like corpses. He stood a while with head hanging, wriggling his fingers; then he sighed, and the sigh turned to a hoarse groan.

From then on he went out almost every night, unnoticed by anyone. He walked up to the tumulus, roughly crumpling his shirt at the chest. But the ploughed strip of land lay a deathly black beyond the tumulus; it was shaggy with grasses, and the wind dried its clods and sent the twiggy melilot swaying.

The steppe hay mowing began just before Trinity Sunday. Stepan and Afonka agreed to do their mowing together. They drove out into the steppe. But the very first night Stepan's oxen wandered off from the spot where they had been grazing.

They sought the animals for several days, roaming the length and width of the district, searching every ravine and gully. They found not a trace of the oxen. Late one afternoon Stepan returned home, flung his jerkin round him and stood at the door without looking back.

'I shall go to the Ukrainian settlements,' he said. 'If anyone's taken them they'll be there.'

'Take some bread, some dry bread for the road,' his old wife fussed over him.

'I'm off!' Stepan answered, knitting his brows. He went out, swinging a stick and slashing off the heads of the worm-wood.

Outside the village he fell in with Afonka.

'Going to the Ukrainians, Stepan?'

'That's the idea.'

'Well, God grant you find your oxen.'

'Christ save you.'

'I've left the scythe in the steppe; when you come back we'll drive them out there,' Afonka called after him.

Stepan waved without turning round. By noon he had reached the village of Lower Yablonovska, and dropped in to see an old comrade of his own regiment. They shared each other's sorrows, he had a drink of milk, and went on his way.

On the road he frequently fell in with people. He would stop them and ask:

'You haven't had oxen come wandering your way, by any chance? One with a broken horn, both of them reddish brown.'

'No, we haven't.'

'Haven't seen them.'

'We haven't noticed any cattle like that.'

So he continued searching along the grey streak of the road, tapping with his stick, sweating, licking his parched lips with his rough tongue.

As evening was coming on, he overtook a wagon loaded with hay at a fork in the road. On top of the hay a flaxen-haired, bare-headed child about three years old was sitting. The horse was being led by a man in greasy canvas trousers and a workman's straw hat. Stepan drew level with him.

'Good day to you.'

The hand carrying the knout was reluctantly raised to the broad brim of the straw hat.

'You haven't chanced to see oxen. . . .' Stepan began, but stopped short. The blood roared in his head, it left his cheeks white as it rushed to his heart: under the straw hat was a face he knew only too well. The face which had shone like a white flame in the darkness of his sleepless nights, had gleamed inflexibly before his eyes. Tired, unsuspecting eyes gazed at him unconcernedly under the shady brim of the hat; thin, burnt whiskers hung over half-open lips; there were gaps in the rows of yellow, smoke-stained teeth.

'Ah! So fate has brought us together again!'

Under the hat, first the sunburnt forehead turned pale, then the pallor slipped slowly over the man's cheeks, to reach his chin and speckle his lips.

'Can you guess who I am?' Stepan demanded.

'What d'you . . . what do you want? I've never seen you before.'

'You haven't? But how about the grain last winter? Who . . . ?'

'It wasn't me. . . . I think you've made a mistake.'

Stepan pulled out a three-pronged fork stuck into the hay and shifted his grip to the stock, not far from the handle.

The Tauridan unexpectedly squatted down by the hoofs of the sweating horse, pressed his palms into the dust and sat there, gazing up at Stepan.

'My wife's died. . . . My little son's all I have left . . .' he said in a horrifyingly indifferent tone, pointing with a trembling finger at the wagon.

'What did you do it for?' Stepan asked hoarsely, shaking all over.

The Tauridan stared down numbly at his canvas trousers, swaying as he squatted.

'Daddy, take my horse. . . . I needed the grain. . . . Take my horse. For Christ's sake! Let there be nothing between us. . . . Let's make it up . . .' he mumbled hurriedly, stumbling over his tongue and scrabbling with his hand in the road dust.

'You did me a wrong! Now my land's lying dead. Well? We've been starving. . . . We've swollen with eating grass! Well?' Stepan shouted, slowly moving closer to the man.

'I buried my wife. . . . She had woman's sickness. . . . There's my boy. . . . Three years old last Easter. . . . Forgive me, daddy! Let's part in peace. . . . I'll hand back the grain.' In his mortal fear the Tauridan nodded his head and babbled away senselessly, his tongue frozen stiff in the grip of his elemental terror.

'Pray to God!' Stepan sighed, crossing himself.

'Stop! Wait! In God's name I ask. . . . How about the boy?'

'I'll take him into my home. . . . You needn't grieve over him!'

'I haven't carted home the hay. . . . Oh! My farm will go to ruin. . . . And how can. . . ?'

Stepan raised the fork, held it above his head for a brief moment, then, feeling a rising roar in his ears, thrust it with a groan into the soft body writhing between the prongs.

He flung a handful of hay over the severe, yellowing face pressed against the ground, then climbed on to the wagon and took the child, who had buried himself in the hay, into his arms.

He walked away from the wagon with reeling, drunken steps, making towards the lights of the settlement glimmering on the rise. Pressing the shuddering child to his chest, he whispered through his chattering teeth:

'Be quiet, little son! Quiet! Now . . . Stop it, or a wolf will get you. Stop it!'

But the child, rolling his eyes, tried to break away from his arms, and his howl rang over the inviolably calm, azure-shadowed steppe:

'Daddy! . . . Daddy! . . . Daddy!'

1925/1926

Concerning the Don Food Requisitioning Committee

The Misadventures of Comrade Ptitsin: Assistant Food Commissar for the Don

I, Ignat Ptitsin, a Cossack of the Provatorov district, was a fine fellow. At my belt I had a Mauser in a wooden holster and two grenades, over my shoulder was a rifle; I had pockets stuffed with cartridges, as well as my cartridge wallet, with the result that my trousers wouldn't stay up, and I was constantly tying them up with string. My eyes were quick and merry; but they had a sort of queer look, and the women used to be frightened by them. I'd say something to one of them when we were on the march, and when she came round she'd say: 'Pfooh, Ignat, what animal eyes you've got! When you look into them you can never see to the bottom.'

Still everything else about me was satisfactory: my voice was a little hoarse, it suited me down to the ground.

In those days I had a food requisitioning job in the Tepipinsk district.

It was in the spring of 1920. In Provatorov a close friend of mine, named Goldin, was collecting grain. He was the same rank as me, and of the Jewish persuasion. Not a bad lad as lads go, but as fiery as gunpowder and cunning beyond all belief. I'm a straight sort, there's no nonsense with me, I collected the grain with a high hand. I'd go along with my angels to see a Cossack, one of the richer ones, and start off with the ultimatum: 'Grain!' 'Haven't any!' 'What d'you mean, you haven't any?' 'What I say, I haven't got any, you snake,' he'd answer. Well, of course, I show no pity, I'd thrust my Mauser into his belly and say in a weary sort of voice: 'I've got ten bullets in this automatic; I'll kill you ten times

125

over, I'll bury you ten times over and dig you up again. Going to bring in the grain?' 'Very good!' he'd say, 'glad to oblige. I'll bring it!'

But as for Goldin, you could crawl into one of his nostrils and out of the other; he was a damnable dry sort, like a goose, but he always managed to harvest more grain than me. But we were both shown the same respect. Goldin for his virginity, for he was as quiet as a girl; and as for me, let them just try not showing me respect! I'm a straight sort; when I start swearing, when I begin to show my teeth, everybody has to laugh at my artistry; the young Cossacks even keep their grain deliberately, they like me to shake them up. 'Why,' they used to say, 'our Ptitsin's singing away like a lark.' That's what they used to call me: a lark. Well okay! And so we were obtaining food for the Ninth Army of the Southern Front when we heard that in Vioshenska district insurgents had joined up with General Sekretiov and were pressing on our people. But then we advanced; we advanced and there was no stopping us. And afterwards we were sent to Kursk province. There we pumped out the grain beautifully. A whole month we pumped, and then another. Before we arrived the authorities used to collect in terms of thousands; but when we turned up we began collecting in two hundred thousands. Meanwhile Goldin was climbing higher and higher, and one fine day we woke up to find he was like a chick hatched out of an egg: now he was the plenipotentiary of the special food-requisitioning commission for supplying the Army of the Southern Front. Okay. I was with my detachment of sailors, scraping up millet and rye in the Kursk province. Goldin sends for me and says quietly: 'Ptitsin, you're a harsh man and you're good at forcing people into the yoke. You're a queer fellow, there's no flabbiness in you at all.' I didn't know quite what he meant by the yoke, but it's true I'm not flabby. I'm all muscle. What do I want to be flabby for? Am I a woman? And no one imagines he can hold back his grain because I'm flabby. 'You look out,' Goldin says, 'be rather more tactful.' But I tell him: 'Do you know that in the October Revolution I took the Kremlin from the Junkers?' 'Yes, I know.' 'And do you know,' I say, 'that when we stormed the Kremlin a Junker's bullet lodged in my bladder and it's still rolling about there, like a goose egg?' 'I know,' he says, 'and I've got very great respect for the bullet in your bladder.' 'All right, you needn't be sorry for my bullet, it's being covered with fat, and sooner or later the blood will draw it out, if not from my heel, then somewhere else. But you feel sorry for our fighters, who're at the front; and make sure they don't go hungry.' 'You can go,' he says, shaking his head and breathing heavily. So perhaps he was beginning to sort of feel sorry for the fighters, or something? Okay. I go back and pump out the grain. And I pumped so hard that all the peasant had left to him was his skin. And I'd have stripped him of that con- venience, I'd have taken it for felt boots. But then Goldin was transferred to Saratov. A week later I got a telegram from him: 'Come to the Don Food Committee, Saratov, to be at my disposition.' It was signed 'Food Commissar for the Saratov Province: Goldin.'

Okay. We travelled to Saratov by goods wagon.

I got separated from my detachment because of the lice. I went to a station to give them a steaming in the bathhouse. I get rid of them there and sit laughing to myself. 'Look what I've grown used to, who I've been living with, who I've been travelling about the world with!' But meanwhile the detachment packed up and rode off. Okay.

I arrive in Saratov. I didn't find Goldin there, nor any Don Food Committee. I asked: 'Where have they got to?' I was told: 'Goldin's been sent to Tambov to work as a Commissar, and the Food Committee has followed him.' Okay. 'But by the way,' they say to me, 'you go along to the Don Executive Committee, you'll find out there.' 'Where is the Don Executive Committee?' 'In Hotel Russia.' Okay. I go along there. 'Is this the Don Executive Committee?' 'Yes,' they answer. 'Second floor, number three.' I go up and tap with my nail on the door: 'May I come in?' 'Please, by all means.' I go in and see a tiny little room, and two people in it. One was a swarthy sort with a little beard, a civilian by the look of him, and the other was an elegant young lady sitting at a typewriter. 'Excuse me,' I say, 'it looks like I've got the wrong number.' And I wave my arm round the room. 'But are you the Don Executive Committee?' 'We are,' he says. 'I'm the chairman, Medvediev, and this is my technical worker.' 'But I,' I say proudly, 'am Ignat Ptitsin of the Don Food Committee. Ever heard of me? No? Pity! You live at a very low level, comrade Medvediev.' He shrugs his shoulders: 'I agree, but it can't be helped; you can't get higher than you can jump.' 'You don't know where our Don Food Committee is?' I ask. 'I haven't the least idea,' he said in a mournful tone and invites me to sit down on an empty chair. Of course I sat down.

I explain that it appears the Don Food Committee has gone to Tambov. Medvediev was quite delighted. 'You don't say! I'm very glad! So I've got the Don Food Committee in Tambov, the Don Land Department in Penza, the administration is in Tula. But where's the military?' He bends back his fingers, counting them, and asks the elegant young lady: 'Tell me, where is our military department?' But she only smiles tenderly and says: 'I can't imagine!'

They were so glad to see me, they'd grown so bored with not seeing people, that they gave me a glass of tea. They gave me tea, but they forgot the sugar. Okay. I started to boil, and said: 'Excuse me, I never drink more than two glasses.' They took fright and started putting sugar in my glass, but I said sternly: 'Write me a letter to Tambov.'

And then I rode off. I found the boys in Tambov, and soon after that the Whites started retreating to the sea, and we, the Don Food Committee, were sent to Rostov.

Goldin managed to get away; he said the horizons were expansive in this sort of work, I'll go to Siberia. His assistant also got away. After they left there were nine changes of these assistants. It was getting near my turn. Okay. According to seniority. So I waited impatiently for the day when the last assistant would flee. He fled from Filinovsk back to Tambov; I gave him a lamb cutlet and a pound of tobacco from my ration to go. And I became the 'Vice' Commissar of the Don Food Committee. Okay, I think, I'll arrive in Rostov, and there I'll put the screw on. We had two trucks: one full of men and the other full of books. Moscow had sent us newspapers and books before we left.

We travelled to Tsaritsin. The Whites had blown up a bridge. We got to the other side walking along planks. We came to a station and took over two trucks. But there was nothing to shift them with, no engine. Now what were we to do? We thought and thought, and harnessed a couple of oxen and a camel to each truck, fitted up drivers' seats on the buffers and drove away.

I, of course, sat on a camel, between his humps; it was warm and didn't rock.

And that's how we crossed every bridge in the district; we harnessed camels or oxen to the trucks and on we went.

However, two days later I fell ill. I felt a stab in my back. Death looked me in the eyes. The lads advised me to stay behind with the locals and come along later, otherwise I'd only snuff out in the truck. Okay! But the pain left me without any strength.

They carried me to a village not far from the railway and told a woman, one of the villagers: 'Look after him, auntie; we'll repay you later.'

But this widow woman turned out to be a settler returned from Siberia. She was a healthy bitch, about fifty years old, and she had a mug not like a woman's but a skewbald horse's. Great nostrils, slanting eyes you could only have stuffed them with straw.

As soon as the lads had gone she started her song: 'It's a boring life for me, living alone; you get well, soldier boy, we'll marry and you'll run the farm. My husband died last year, but there's plenty of juice left in me yet.'

But what if she was full of juice! It wasn't any use to me. Well, I drop down on the bed and lie ill. The old bag pestered me continually: 'Shall we get married in the summer?' 'I'll marry you,' I tell her, 'you speckled cow; slaughter a sheep and feed me up, otherwise there'll be nothing for you to marry.'

She slaughtered a sheep, she fed me up. I lay unconscious and ate mutton wholesale. But she keeps on at me in her Siberian fashion, calling me her young man. 'Ah,' I think, 'I'm my own young man, as God loves my mother! I'll be done for like the lice if I sleep with such a carcass.' For she must have gone over three hundred pounds. Okay. I ate one of her sheep, but she didn't want to slaughter a second.

'What,' I say to her, 'you fat old witch, you don't want to?

D'you think I can get well by starving?' 'You'll get through a whole leg of mutton today, and another tomorrow, and I've only got five lambs on the farm,' 'You and your lambs can perish,' I said. 'I'm clearing out.'

And I went. I spent a day getting ready and went. I caught up with my detachment just outside Rostov.

So I arrive in Rostov. I abandoned the detachment and went straight to the chairman.

'Hello,' I say to him. 'We,' I say, 'are the deputy of the Don Food Commissar.' The chairman takes off his spectacles and polishes and polishes them. At last he asks: 'You're not ill, are you, comrade?' 'No,' I say, 'I've got well.' 'Where've you come from?' 'From the station.' 'But what Don Commissar?' he asks, and he gets so wild he starts turning as blue as a plum. 'You're joking, surely?' 'Where's the joke?' I say. 'We've come from Kursk, here's the seals of the Don Food Commissariat.' I take them out of my pocket and fling them on the table. 'And the books are with the lads at the station.' 'Go to Moscow Street,' he says, 'and take a look at the real Don Food Commissar. He's been functioning for the last six weeks. But as for you, I don't know you.'

The sweat rolled off me and down my shirt. I go with the lads from the station to Moscow Street. 'Is this the building of the Don Food Commissariat?' 'Yes.' Blessed mother! I see an ordinary building of five floors, and as many people in them as sunflower seeds. Elegant young ladies typing away on typewriters. Abacuses rattling. Our hair stood on end. I go inside to see the Food Commissar, to tell him he hadn't any right to be sitting there.

But he answers quietly, with a smile: 'You might have been six months on your journey, and we'd have had to go on waiting for you here. Go to Salsk district as our agent,' he says. Okay. Of course, I was furious. I set my arms akimbo and told him: 'Any uneducated person can sign papers with pen and ink. You and your book-keepers, your elegant young ladies with finger-nails! You should try climbing over the corn bins till all your holes are filled with dust!'

And we rode off. What can you do with a blockhead like that? He'll never understand. But as I left I thought seriously:

In this province the work's gone to pot. A soft voice, and a learned man by the look of him! What sort of Commissar will he make? You won't get so much as a stone out of people with your soft speaking. When I barked I used to get something done. We didn't have any book-keepers, or young ladies with finger-nails. No, we didn't. But we got the job done!

1923–25

On Kolchak, Nettles and
other Things

Now look, citizen world . . . I mean citizen people's judge . . . at
the meeting you explained all about the law as it applies to the
rich peasants' shameful wrecking activities. Now I want to
clear up the position in regard to nettles and other things.
. . . I think that under the Soviet government people oughtn't
to get the sort of treatment I've had from citizens. Though
that's just the point: if they had been citizens it wouldn't have
been so bad. But they were women! After that life's hardly
worth living, believe me!

In the spring our own Nastya turned up in the village. She'd
been living in the mining area, but then she took it into her
head to come back to us: the devil dragged her by her skirt
tails.

So one day our chairman, Steshka, comes along to see me.
We shake hands, and he says:

'You know Nastya's come back from the mines, Fiodot.
With her hair cut short and wearing a red kerchief.'

Well, wearing a kerchief or not, what was it to do with me?
Of course it was shameful for a woman to have her hair cut
short. But he didn't go on, so I asked:

'Has she come to visit her family, or what?'

'Visit her family!' he says. 'Why, she's going to get our
women into a herd, she's going to start an organization among
them. Keep both your eyes skinned, and look out for yourself!
Just you lay a finger on your woman and they'll have you by
the tail, you son of a bitch, and put you in the doghouse.'

So we talked about one thing and another, and then he made
a suggestion:

'Drive her to the district, Fiodot. She's got a document
and she's got to go there to take over a woman's post, something

on the lines of a women's executive committee, or the devil knows what. Drive her there out of respect for me.'

So I had to reason with him:

'It's respect for you, Stepan, but for me it's a sheer insult. It isn't convenient to take a horse off work when we're so busy in the fields.'

'Please yourself,' he says, 'but take her.'

So this Nastya of ours comes along to my hut. So as not to be upset by the sight of her short hair, I kept my eyes lowered, and went off into the steppe to get the mare. But I must tell you my mare was born of a real gypsy; when she runs the earth quakes; when she lies down she stays put for three days: in a word, help her to get up and we'll get rid of her! I don't know how many times I've felt like raising an axe against her, but I felt sorry for her: she's in foal.

Now while I was catching her and arguing with her – stop kicking, you fool, you're not taking any old body, but the female authority – Nastya and my dear wife were putting their heads together.

'Does your husband beat you?' Nastya asks.

And my fool of a wife, she says straight out:

'Yes, he does.'

And no sooner had I brought the mare back to the yard than Nastya starts on me:

'What do you beat your wife for?'

'For the sake of order. If you don't beat her she'll go bad. A woman's like a horse; you have to beat her or she won't move.'

'You've no right to beat a horse, let alone your wife!' So she starts giving me lessons.

We had a little talk, and then off we went. Only, I was artful: I didn't take a knout with me. So we go along at a walking pace, we drive so slow we might be carrying earthenware pots.

'Drive faster,' Nastya says.

'How can I drive faster if I mustn't whip the mare?'

She said nothing, only pursed her lips. She sat perfectly still; and that was just what I wanted. I lay down in the back of the cart and had a doze. The mare, not being a fool, came to a stop. And would you believe it, citizen, or whatever you're

called, Nastya takes a handful of hay and goes in front of the
mare, tickling and tickling her. But it's a good twelve miles
to the district. So we didn't arrive till next morning. And
Nastya was crying. She called me a scoundrel. But I said to
her:

'Call me a pot if you like, so long as you don't put me in the
oven.'

On the way back I was mad with rage. I broke off a switch
almost as thick as a telegraph pole, and laid on the mare so
hard that the dust flew out of her tail:

'So you wanted equality? Here it is, take it!'

When we drove into the yard I called to the wife:

'Unharness the mare, you old so and so.'

'You're not a lord,' she retorts, and waves me away from the
door.

I go up to her and seize her by the hair. . . . But then what
happened! It was absolutely indecent! In the past she'd
been afraid of me, and hadn't dared blink. But now, for no
reason whatever, she tugged at my beard and called me all
sorts of foreign words. And in front of the children, too! And
I've got one girl of marriageable age. My wife was quite strong,
and she could easily scratch me: and how! She made the fur
fly, and I crawled away from her like a snake out of a hole. And
it was all through that Nastya, the short-haired hussy!

From then on there was a sort of civil war between us. Not
a day passed without me and my stupid fool of a wife fighting all
day, and the work went to pot. We fought to the last ruthless
shout. And on the Sunday she gathered her things together,
collected the children, took something from the farm and went
and settled in the former landowner's stables.

At one time, in the old days, a landowner lived in our village.
The Reds frightened him away, and he flew off to warm countries. Educated people do say that overseas the starlings and
landowners have a good life. We burnt down his house,
but the stables weren't touched. They were brick, with good
floors. And so my flighty wife went and settled in those stables.
I was left alone, like a boil in a visible spot. In the morning I
set out to milk the cow, but damn her, she didn't want even to
look at me. I tried getting at her all sorts of ways, but she

134

wouldn't recognize me as one of the family! Somehow I hobbled her and tied her to the fence.

'Stand still,' I said, 'you lop-eared devil, or you'll get on my nerves, and I may do you in!'

I pushed the bucket under her belly and was starting to feel her teat, quite gently, when she swung her tail and lashed me in the eyes with her filthy brush. Merciful God, I was all ready to approach her with a prayer; but after the way she lashed out at me I swore at her, sinner that I am, and organized an All Souls' Day for her, a real true remembrance of the dead!

I screwed up my eyes, drew my cap down over them and began tugging at the teat, this way and that. The milk went squirting outside the bucket, while she lashed away at me on both cheeks with her tail. I couldn't see a thing, I was all prepared to leave the bucket and run blindly out of the yard, when she, the carrion, kicked out with her hoof and sent the very last little drop flying over. I swore at her, hung the empty bucket on her horn and went off to clean myself up.

Believe me, since that day the whole of our life in the village has been turned upside down. Some five days later my neighbour Anisim thought he would reprove his wife, to stop her making eyes at the young men of the village of an evening.

'You wait, Dunia,' he says, 'I'll take the saddle-girth down from the cart, and we'll have a little fun and games with you.'

As soon as she heard that she flung up her tail and ran to join my fool of a woman in the stable. Some days later I heard that Steshka's wife and sister-in-law had left him and settled in the stables with the others. And then two more women joined them. Altogether some eight of them were gathered there, living in a herd, and doing nothing, while we and our farms were perishing. You could either plough without eating first, or if you preferred it you could eat and not plough, or you could crawl with both feet into the noose.

So we men got together one evening on the ledge outside the hut, to talk over our sorrows, and I said:

'Brothers, how long are we going to go on suffering this torment? Let's go and drive them out of the stables and drag them home complete with their innards.'

So we got ready and went. We wanted to make Steshka

the chairman commander of the task force, but he refused on the grounds that he was tetchy and was always having to hold back his quarrelsome nature.

'I,' he says, 'am a young bindweed and very quarrelsome, and so I'm not really suitable. But you, Fiodot, shed your blood for the Soviet régime; and besides, you've got a face just like Kolchak, so it's more in your line.'

We go along to the stable, and I say:

'Let's avoid any scandalous quarrelling, at first at any rate. I shall go to them as a sort of delegate, and I'll tell them they can all come home: we've proclaimed an amnesty for them.'

I crawled through the fence and went to the stable. My detachment lay down in reserve by the ditch, and had a smoke.

No sooner had I opened the door than Steshka's wife came at me:

'What have you come for, you blood-sucker?'

Before I could open my mouth all the women seized hold of me and started dragging me mercilessly around the stable. Then they stood round me in a ring and howled, and my old hag the worst of the lot:

'What have you come here for, you son of a bitch?'

And I answer in all goodness of heart:

'Stop playing about, women. An amnesty . . .'

I'd no sooner said that word than Anisim's wife flew at me with her fists raised:

'A whole lifetime you've treated us like cattle, you've beaten us, sworn at us; and now you come all nice and smarmy! Here, taste this! You're an amnesty yourself, but we're honest women!' I start leaking between the legs, and she turns to the others: 'What shall we do with him, women, for his leaking?'

My heart sank. Now, I thought, they'll put me to shame, the filthy hussies!

Even now my inside turns over as I recall it. It was shameful. They laid me out on the floor without the least sign of shame. Dunia Anisimova sat on my head and said:

'Don't be afraid, Fiodot; we'll treat you with homely remedies, to make you remember we're not street hussies but married women!'

Only how can you call them homely remedies when they

were nettles? And wild nettles at that: the devil had grown them for seed, they were over two feet high! Afterwards I couldn't sit down like a human being for a week; I had to sit on my belly. . . . Their homely remedies gave me blisters all over.

Next day there was a village meeting, and a resolution was passed that women were no longer to be beaten, and a couple of acres were to be ploughed up and sown with sunflower seeds for their women's executive committee. The women all came back home, mine too. But to this day I'm living a dog's life. For instance, I see the calves nibbling at the cabbages in the garden, and I call to my son, Grishka: 'Go and drive them out.' But he, the brat, answers:

'Daddy, why do they tease you about Kolchak?'

When I walk along the street the children won't let me pass: 'Kolchak! Kolchak! How did you wage war on the women?'

And don't you think that's shameful? All my life I've occupied myself with farming, and now suddenly I'm changed into Kolchak. That's what they call Steshka's mongrel, and so I'm on the same level as a dog, am I? No. . . . I'm not standing for it! And that's why I ask you: if I complain in court about the women, perhaps, citizen judge, you can find a suitable law to apply to them for calling me by a dog's name, 'Kolchak', and similar nettling insults?

1926

The One Language

The Lushin district centre is half buried under an old filthy layer of snow; the recently arrived rooks wear new plumage the colour of burnished steel.

The smoke from the chimneys is fragile and thin. The sky is grey. The outlines of the houses seem to be dissolving in the mist. Only beyond the river is the undulating ridge of the Don-side hills clear and distinct, and the forest stands out as if it were sketched in Chinese ink.

In the People's House a district congress of Soviets is meeting. It has just begun. The secretary of the Party Regional Committee is making a report on the international situation. The delegates are sitting on the benches, and looking at them from behind you see red-banded Cossack caps, plain fur caps, fur caps with ear flaps, rows of short tanned sheepskin jackets. One single heavy breathing. Occasionally a cough. Not many beards, the men are mainly clean-shaven, with and without various shades of whiskers.

The secretary reads Chamberlain's note. From the back rows comes a fiery:

'Let him stop barking!'

The chairman knocks his glass against the water carafe:

'Order! . . .'

During the half-hour break which followed the report, when the tobacco smoke was floating over the fur caps in the vestibule, through the roar of voices I heard a familiar tone – surely it was Maidannikov's? I pushed my way through my neighbours. Maidannikov had been elected chairman of the Soviet of Pieschany hamlet for a further term. He was surrounded by a little group of Cossacks. The youngest of them, who was wearing a fairly new Budionny cloth helmet, was saying:

'And we'll fight. . . .'

138

'But they'll twist our tails. . . .'

'But what happened last time?'

'They've got the technique, brother.'

'Technique without the people is like a horse without a Cossack.'

'But they aren't short of people, are they?'

Maidannikov began to speak again. His voice was thick and soft, like good cart grease.

'That's enough! You're right off the mark, comrade villager. If war does come, it won't frighten us. . . . Now, wait a bit! Let me finish. When I've done threshing you can start pouring out. But now listen. We were called up for the German war in 1915. I was in the third draft. Our company went straight from Kamenska district to the front. They tacked us on to the eighth infantry division, and we marched with them as if buckled on. We took our share in battles. Not far from Styr we were parted from our horses. They thrust bayonets on our rifles, and we were turned into foot-sloggers. We fought . . . in the trenches and in other ways. But most of all in the trenches. We spent a whole year in the blasted mud. And four months without relief. The lice swarmed over us. Partly out of our misery, partly because we went unwashed. And the lice were of all sorts: those born of misery are bare-backed, but those born of dirt are black and almost as big as beetles. Though there were these different sorts, we fed them all alike; we used to take off our shirts and spread them out on the ground; and when you pressed a flask over them or a shell case they turned all bloody at once. We beat the lice with sticks, with our belts. We killed them like animals. That'll tell you how many of them there were. They wandered about our shirts in droves.

'But we went on fighting. What for, how and why, no one knew. We supped on broth others had cooked.

'After a year of this I was filled with yearning. Death – and nothing else. I longed for my horse – we didn't see them for months on end, and we wondered how they were being looked after. And back home my family was left in I didn't know what state. But the main thing was: what were the people – and I among them – facing death for? We just didn't know.

'In 1916 we were withdrawn from the front and taken back about twenty-five miles. Reinforcements arrived for our company, almost all of them old men. Beards down below their navels, and all the rest of it. We had a bit of a break, we could see to our horses. And then: a bomb! An order arrived from the divisional staff to move our company up to the front line. It appeared the soldiers up there were in revolt; they didn't want to go into the trenches, to lie in the mud; they had no desire to rub shoulders with death.

'Our captain, Dimbash, gave us a long explanation. But I took it on myself to write him a note and tossed it out of the crowd:

' "Your Excellency, you've explained to us about the war, how the peoples of various languages are fighting one another. But how can we go and fight our own people?" As he read the note his face changed, and he had nothing to say. And then we chewed over the question why they'd sent old Cossacks into our company, many of them Old Believers into the bargain. They were all for the Tsar and would be for him more and more. It was one thing to be old: they'd been trained in the old service. But it was another thing for us, a bit stupid as we were, worn out with active service. That was just it: in those years a man lost his senses in a regiment quicker than you can whet a scythe.

'We were driven up to attack the soldiers. We had four machine guns and an armoured car. We drove up to the spot where a regiment was in revolt, and we found two companies of Kuban Cossacks already there; and others too, pock-marked and looking like Kalmiks, surrounding this regiment. It was a terrible business, brothers. Behind a wood two batteries were unlimbered; but the regiment was standing in a glade and the men were murmuring. Officers rode up to them and tried to win them over, but they just stood and muttered.

'Our captain gave us the order, we unsheathed our sabres, and, riding at a trot, surrounded the regiment with horses. . . . The Kubans went too. And the soldiers started throwing down their rifles. They flung them down in heaps, and started murmuring again.

'But my blood was boiling till my lips burned with salt. How could I drive any man into that grave, when I myself had spent part of my life there, had lived in the ground like a marmot? When we galloped up I saw a Cossack in our troop, Filimonov, strike a soldier on the face furiously with the flat of his sabre. And right before my eyes the man's face swelled and streamed with blood, and he was frightened. A young soldier, and I could see he was frightened. I felt cold all over; I couldn't control myself, and I rode up to them:

' "Chuck it, Filimonov!" He swore at me, though he was an Old Believer. I raised my sabre, thinking I'd frighten him. "Chuck it," I said, "or by God I'll cut you down." He tore the rifle off his shoulder. I thrust the point of my sabre into his throat. I took aim as if he was a stuffed sack, but it was a living man I removed from the earth. . . . And what happened after that would have been impossible even for the devil to tell. The Kuban Cossacks opened fire on us, and we on them. The pock-marked ones galloped into the attack against us, but the soldiers snatched up their rifles, started revolting again and opened fire on the cavalry. That shows how much they were worked up.

'We were withdrawn from that spot. At first we were to be sent to the rear; but before we could gasp we found our-selves in the Carpathians: we hadn't time to get the lice off our trousers when there were the Carpathians. We travelled by night along the lines of communication. Our orders were: not a sound, not a jingle. It turned out the Austrian trenches were some three hundred feet from ours. We lived a whole day not raising our heads. It rained. We were wet, with mud over our ankles in the trenches. I couldn't get any sleep or rest. It was murder! "How come," I was thinking, "that we're living in an embrace with death in these trenches?" I began to think hard of having a talk with the Austrians. Their soldiers sort of talked our language. Sometimes they would shout across in Polish: "Sir, what are you fighting for?" But we'd shout back: "And what are you fighting for?" We couldn't come to any decision because of the distance between us. So I thought: now if only we really could get together and talk it all over! But there wasn't any possibility. We were separated by the barbed wire, like cattle; and yet those Austrians were just the same as us. We'd all been driven off the land, like children from the titty. We ought to be able to find a common language.

'And then one morning we wake up, and the guard shouts: "Look, boys, an animal's got caught on our wire." And we could hear the Austrians bawling away like rooks at harvest time. So I raised my head a little, and right opposite me I see an elk, an animal. You know, it's a sort of reindeer, with bushy horns. And he'd got entangled in the wire by his horns. Along the front to the left of us heavy fighting was going on, and the firing had driven him in between the two lines of trenches.

'The Austrians shouted: "Sirs, rescue the animal; we won't shoot." I flung on my greatcoat and climbed on to the breastwork. I looked across at their trenches, and they were lined with heads. As soon as I went close to the animal he reared up, shaking the stakes and supporting spurs. Three other Cossacks came out to give me a hand. But there was nothing we could do, he wouldn't let us get near him. Then I saw some Austrians running up without their rifles, and one of them had a pair of wire cutters.

'And that gave us the chance to start talking. Our company commander climbed on to the breastwork and took aim at the end Austrian, but I covered him with my back. Our officers couldn't get us to break up the party, and we brought the Austrians back to our trenches as guests. I started talking to one of them, but I couldn't say a word either in their language or in our own, my tears choked me. I got lined up with an Austrian, no longer young, red-haired. I seated him on a cartridge chest and said: "Look, sir, how can you and I be enemies, we're related. Look, the callouses are still on our hands." He couldn't understand what I was saying, but I could see he understood with his heart. And I scratched the callouses on his hand. He nodded: "Yes, I know, I agree." And a group of Cossacks and the Austrian soldiers gathered round us. And I said: "Sir, we don't want anything of yours, and don't you touch anything of ours! Let's put an end to the war." I could see he agreed with me again, but he didn't understand a word, and so he beckoned to us to go over to his trenches. He explained: "There's one of us who can talk Russian there." So we went. All our company pulled out and went across! Our officers got the wind up. We came to the Austrian trenches. They'd got a Czech there who could talk Russian. I talked away to my Austrian, and this Czech translated. I repeated what I'd said about our not being enemies but relations. And I again scratched the callouses on his hand with my nail and clapped him on the back. Through the Czech he answered: "I'm a worker, a locksmith, and I thoroughly agree with you." I said to him: "Let's put an end to the war, brothers. It's a filthy business. And we ought to be sticking our bayonets into those who set us against each other." These words of mine even moved him to tears. He answered that he'd left a wife and child at home, and he agreed to end the war. We raised a great shout. But their officer strutted around like a turkey cock, baring his teeth, the swine. We fraternized and had a drink of wine with them. And we found one language for the whole lot of us, so that when I said something to them they understood everything just as I said it, without any interpreter; they talked and cried and started kissing us.

'When I got back to our trenches I took the bolt out of my rifle, trod it in the mud and swore by God I wouldn't fire again at my Austrian brothers: at the locksmith, the worker, the farmer. . . . That same night our company left the trenches; we were disarmed not far from the village of Shavelko. But soon after that the Revolution came, and they dealt with the Tsar in Petersburg. . . .'

'Wait a bit,' the young Cossack in the Budionny cloth helmet interrupted him. 'Tell us what happened to the animal.'

'The animal? We rescued him. He galloped away as far as we could see him. With a load of barbed wire on his horns. But the point of all this isn't the animal. Here were people talking the one language, but just now you started burbling: "War, war." We know what the war will be like: when we come up to their soldiers we'll strike callous against callous, and we'll start talking.'

'Comrade delegates, come along!' someone shouted from the stage in the hall, ringing a bell.

Pushing open the door, to a roar of conversation, the solid mass of delegates poured back into the hall.

1927

Soft-hearted

'Change at Gryazy.'

The booking-clerk thrust a ticket and the change through the window, and slammed the small door. Ignat Ushakov put the ticket carefully into the side pocket of his coat and, smoking as he went, walked on to the platform. Crowds were bustling round the carriage doors, a shunting engine was man-oeuvring somewhere on the track, hooting curtly and hoarsely. A block had formed by the last carriage but one. In the dark-ness a porter's apron showed up white in the light of a lantern; a woman's hysterical voice exclaimed:

'But guard, you must realize that I've got to get on. There's only sixty pounds altogether in that basket.'

'I can't help that, citizeness! Do you understand Russian? I tell you for the tenth time that I can't. You've got three bundles as well as the basket. You can't get all that lot into the carriage.'

'But I shan't have time to put it in the luggage van.'

As Ushakov pushed his way through to the last carriage he saw the guard climb up to the carriage platform and, putting out his lantern, close the door behind him without further argument.

Inside the carriage the air was blue with tobacco smoke. The freshly painted walls smelt of oil paint, and the choking scent of cheap cigarettes came from the berths; someone's sweaty, long unwashed feet gave off a pungent stink. Someone on one of the top berths was asleep, snoring; those below were smoking and talking in undertones. Making himself comfort-able on the other top berth, Ushakov lit another cigarette and, raising his head, saw the tiny lights of the station flowing past; the black outlines of trees flashed by the window, and from time to time a spark, thrown from the engine chimney together with the smoke, fluttered along like an orange butterfly.

The lulling clatter of the wheels made him feel sleepy,

Down below, someone was monotonously telling of last year's harvest and the price of wool. Putting out his cigarette, he drew his coat over his head and dozed off. An hour or so later he was aroused by voices. Someone's disturbingly familiar voice was quietly saying in a sing-song tone:

> '*As our grand-dad Yeremil,*
> *Caught a lot of little ruffs,*
> *He had a whole pound of ruffs,*
> *Then he had two pounds of ruffs,*
> *And then what a lot he had!*
> *And what fine big ruffs he had!*'

The man speaking the verse clapped his hands in time with the rhythm; a young child laughed rapturously, in ringing tones. As soon as the voice singing the children's song stopped, a child cried insistently:

'Daddy, more. . . .'

And then the words again floated gently but importunately into Ushakov's ears:

> '*As our grand-dad Yeremil*
> *Caught a lot of little ruffs . . .*'

Ushakov listened without opening his eyes, trying to identify the voice, to determine to whom, out of all his acquaintance, those familiar yet half-forgotten tones belonged. His memory came to his aid. Mastering his drowsy languor, he opened his eyes. Below him he saw a stocky sailor sitting with legs widespread, gently tossing a curly-haired, rosy cheeked girl, two or three years old. The sailor was smiling good-naturedly as he sang about the ruffs, indicating their size with his hands.

Under the white naval cap Ushakov could see straight black hair, but the face was concealed behind the child's body. For a good minute Ushakov watched the sailor's strong hairy arms tirelessly tossing up the excited child; then he coughed and dropped his legs down over the side of the berth.

'Now, don't get too excited, Tamara my dear,' the sailor said. 'Time for bye-byes. See, we've disturbed an uncle. Look out, or he'll hurt you.'

Cautiously letting himself down from his berth, Ushakov

took a sidelong glance at the sailor and raised his eyebrows in astonishment:

'Why, Vladimir, is it you?'

'My God! . . . This is an unexpected meeting.'

They embraced and kissed each other. Leaning back and smiling, the sailor grasped Ushakov's hand firmly, gave him a long look and shook his head:

'Just the same! Not changed at all! Only grown up and filled out. To think of it! We haven't seen each other since 1917, and now. . . . Why, you were still a boy then.'

A young woman sitting on the opposite berth sat watching them with interest. The sailor seemed unusually animated, fidgety, as though he were a little embarrassed. Through his expressions of noisy pleasure sounded an artificial, unnatural note. Ushakov was coldly restrained, as though on his guard.

'I can guess. . . . The very same chin, the same eyes. You haven't changed in the least. You've a startling resemblance to your father. Even in those days I said you were like him. My God, how many years is it since we last saw each other? . . . Eight. . . .'

'Yes, it's a long time.'

'But why haven't I introduced you to each other? This' – he turned to the woman – 'is my first cousin, Ignat Ushakov. And this . . .' – the sailor pointed with a theatrically exaggerated gesture to the young woman – 'this is my family. I hope you'll take to each other.'

Picking up the young child again, he pealed with laughter. The woman held out her hand to Ushakov, and said to the sailor reproachfully, with an embarrassed smile:

'But why are you giving him a false impression?'

Ushakov hardly noticed her remark; he squeezed her cold, slender hand and turned back to his cousin:

'Where've you come from, and where are you going?'

'In sailor lingo, I've weighed anchor and am setting my course for Moscow. But we can talk about me later. How are you and what are you doing? Where are you working? How are you getting on? Are uncle and aunt well? Of course uncle is still busy with his bees, like the old days?'

'Thank you. They're well. Father's still rearing bees.

147

I'm working in the Young Communists' District Committee, in our own district. I've just started a holiday, I'm going to Moscow for a week.'

'So you're climbing, little by little. Great lad, Ignat! Been in the Young Communists' long?'

'Since 1920.'

'And you're a party member, of course?'

'A candidate.'

'So-o!'

Ushakov took out his cigarettes, looked at the child whom her mother was putting down to sleep and suggested:

'Let's go along to the end platform and have a smoke.'

'Come on then, brother; come on. I'm so glad we've met! I find it difficult to believe, honest I do.'

The sailor laughed noisily, giving Ushakov a friendly clap on the back. Knitting his brows, Ushakov went to the door. On the platform at the end of the carriage they lit cigarettes. Ushakov took one draw, then asked his cousin without looking at him:

'Did you serve with the Whites in counter-intelligence?'

The sailor laughed artificially and put his arm round Ushakov's shoulder:

'What's this? An interrogation?'

'Answer, I ask you.'

'Well, yes. . . . I did.'

'Are you living under your own name now?'

'No.'

They were both silent for a few moments, then:

'Where are you working now? In the fleet?'

'You see. . . . I served in the merchant navy, I worked in a port. A dry-land sailor, so to speak. For certain reasons I had to come away from the south. But why do you ask?'

'Because the G.P.U. is looking for you.'

'You don't say?'

'Yes, cousin; I do say.'

'What are they looking along an empty track for? Why, I haven't been in the country for eight years.'

'They simply checked on whether you'd been at home at all during all those years. They asked me about it, too. I didn't know you'd worked in counter-intelligence. At one time we heard rumours that you'd been killed in a battle near Veliko-knyazhevsk. That was at the beginning of 1918, when you retreated with the Volunteer Army. We all thought of you as dead until the G.P.U. discovered that you were a hero of the Whites' counter-intelligence, a rooter-out of sedition, so to speak!'

Ushakov smiled caustically, staring hard at his cousin. The sailor puffed smoke out of his cigarette as he gazed through the window. His small black eyes had a stern look, and for some reason the tightly compressed lips were very slightly smiling.

'Tell me,' Ushakov said, 'how did you come to get into counter-intelligence? What made you do it? I was told that in Makeevka settlement you hanged close on twenty men suspected of being in touch with the Bolsheviks. Is that true?'

Drumming on the glass with his fingers, and speaking slowly, as though cautiously groping for the appropriate words, the sailor answered:

'If you feel like it, listen. . . . At the end of 1917 I had no political opinions or convictions whatever. I was just the same as thousands of other semi-intelligent people. I didn't like the Bolsheviks, I didn't like the Whites. I returned from the German front with a group of soldiers from my own division and got to Rostov-on-Don; then I travelled on to a comrade in Novocherkassk, and joined the Volunteer Army. That came about in a way against my own will. There was simply a surge of patriotic feeling, and under its influence I joined Kornilov. . . . Close to Velikoknyazhevsk I was wounded, was sent to the rear and spent some time in hospital. When I got well I was offered a job in counter-intelligence. But it isn't true, it's a lie that I actively fought against the Bolsheviks. I was a pawn. . . . I was shifted about by forces from above. . . . And it isn't true either that I hanged peasants in Makeevka. The Cossacks hanged them, and I had nothing whatever to do with it. But after that it was the usual story; in the end I lost all faith in the defenders of the "one and indivisible". I saw all the filth of it, and decided to break with the past. When the Whites retreated from the Crimea I remained behind. I couldn't reveal my true name, for I'd have been shot. . . . So I concealed my past; it wasn't difficult to do in those days of confusion. Then I started working in the port, where I met a dear, lovely girl and married her. As you have seen, now I've got a baby daughter, I'm happy, I get my living by work, and, though I'm non-party, I sympathize with all my heart with your ideals. . . .' The sailor flashed his tear-filled eyes at his cousin, and went on: 'My past oppresses me. . . . I hope you believe me? I've finished for ever with my past and I'm trying to redeem my guilt by honest work. I hope you'll do me a brotherly service and won't say any more about it. . . .'

'You're wrong,' Ushakov said, shaking his head nervously. 'I must report on you.'

'In short, you intend to betray me?'

'Don't use fine phrases. I must do what in my place any honest man would do.'

'I've got a wife and child. . . .'

'That has nothing to do with your past activities.'

'Ignat! D'you remember how we grew up together? I was older than you, and your mother used to ask me to look after you. D'you remember how we used to run out into the steppe to break up the starlings' nests? You were so sensitive, so soft-hearted; you cried when I picked up the fledglings. But you're different now. I can see you've got the heart to tear a human nest to pieces and to leave my child an orphan. Well, so be it. All right: at the next station you can report to the G.P.U.' He was silent for a few moments, then he began again: 'But I'm sure you understand. Oh, my God! I've got a baby girl. . . . She'll die of starvation if I . . .'

He covered his face with his hand and began to tremble.

Feeling tears and an uninvited pity rising inside him, Ushakov walked swiftly back to their compartment, and sat down at the window.

'Must I behave like that? Maybe he really has changed. . . .' He glanced sidelong at the child stretched out in sleep. 'And that child will be a living reproach. Oh, hell, what a filthy mess! . . . Should I keep quiet, or not?'

A minute or two later his cousin came back to the compartment. Without looking at Ushakov he began to gather his things together. Then he bent over the sleeping child and gently stroked her on the head. Ushakov turned away. Standing with his back to him, the sailor thrust some documents into the pocket of his white jacket.

'Come outside for a moment,' Ushakov asked.

He hurried, he almost ran, to the platform. His cousin followed him. They halted by the carriage window, where they had stood talking some ten minutes before.

'Listen, Vladimir. . . . I've decided not to say anything. . . .'

'Thank you. . . .'

'I hope we need say no more?'

'Thank you, Ignat. I knew you'd never be a Judas. After all, you realize that without me my family would starve. I've got nobody except you and your people, I haven't any parents, and nor has my wife. Who'd give her anything?'

'That's enough! Go back to the compartment, we'll be arriving at a station in a minute or two.'

'You go back. I'll go to the toilet and have a wash. I'm ashamed to confess it, but I cried like a kid after our talk. My face is all swollen. Not a word to my wife about all this!'

'Why, of course not.'

Ushakov went slowly back to the compartment and, resting his forehead against the window, stared at the brick outbuildings of the station. The train stopped for several minutes; then the wheels began their clatter again, gradually accelerating. The child woke up and disturbed its mother. The woman sat up on the bench, and asked Ushakov:

'But where's your cousin?'

'Vladimir wanted to have a wash. He's got a bit of a headache.'

Some ten minutes passed. There was still no sign of Vladimir. Ushakov went along to see what was happening. The toilet was vacant; there was no one on the end platform either. Thoroughly perplexed, he returned to the compartment.

'You didn't ask your husband to buy something, did you?' he asked the woman. 'Surely he hasn't got left behind at the station?'

'My husband? What husband?'

151

'What d'you mean, what husband?'

'Who are you referring to?'

'Strange! I was talking about Vladimir, my cousin.'

For a second she looked at Ushakov distrustfully, then she laughed openly:

'But you don't seriously take me for your cousin's wife?' she asked between her laughter.

'What are you getting at?'

She shrugged her shoulders and smiled:

'Surely you realized that it was all a joke on your cousin's part? And a rather silly joke at that. What are you staring at me for?'

'But . . . but your daughter called . . . him daddy.'

'Well, what of it? As soon as your cousin got into the carriage he began treating her with sweets, and playing with her. And you know how quickly children can get attached to anyone. Evidently she saw some likeness between your cousin and her father and started calling him daddy. He and I had quite a laugh about it.'

'But pardon me. . . . He told me quite seriously.'

The woman stared at Ushakov again:

'He did, did he? So he didn't explain to you that it was all a joke? My husband is working in Moscow, and I'm on my way to him now.'

She turned away, evidently considering the matter closed. But Ushakov fidgeted with embarrassment, and decided to go back to the toilet. On the shelf by the wash-basin he saw a scrap of paper with writing on it. He automatically picked it up, and read the words, clearly written in copying pencil:

'Thank you for your goodness, Ignat. You're just the same good-hearted boy that you were in the days of our childhood. But all the same I think it wiser to get out before you discover my trick with the "family". Don't be anxious about the "wife"; she has a real husband in Moscow, an assistant book-keeper or something. He'll look after her. Thank you yet again. Maybe we shall meet some time or other.

'Forgive me for putting on this act. I'm an embittered wolf, and I know that in these times you can't trust your own father, let alone your cousin. Accept . . . etc. V.'

152

Ushakov read the note again, and sidled out of the toilet.

Half an hour later the train stopped at a station. Frowning as though he had a bad attack of tooth-ache, Ushakov ran out of the carriage. Seeing the raspberry-coloured cap of an agent of the Transport Section of the G.P.U. on the platform, he made his way towards him.

1927

WARTIME AND POST-WAR ARTICLES, SPEECHES AND SKETCHES

On the Don

The men called up into the Red Army are hurrying along to the square in the district centre; their families are with them to see them off. Two boys aged seven or eight are running along in front of me, hand in hand. Their parents overtake me. He's a big fellow, a tractor-driver by the look of him, in carefully patched blue overalls and a clean shirt. His wife is a swarthy young woman. Her lips are tightly compressed, her eyes are tear-stained. As she draws level with me she says quietly, just to her husband:

'And so they're . . . coming at us again! They wouldn't let us live a quiet life together, would they! But you watch out, Fiodya, don't let them pass.'

The hulking Fiodya wipes his sweating palms with a dirty grease-stained handkerchief, and smiles condescendingly, protectively, as he says in a deep tone:

'You've done nothing but give me instruction all night, and you're still not finished! Now that's enough. I'm educated without your help, and I know my business. You'd do better when you get back home to tell your brigadier that if they go on stacking ricks like those we saw on the road by Rotten Ravine, we'll skin him alive. You just tell him that. Okay?'

The woman tries to say something, but her husband cuts her short angrily, and says in his rumbling bass voice:

'Oh, that's enough of that! Cork it up, for God's sake! When we get to the square they'll tell us better than you can, whatever happens.'

The neat ranks of the mobilized men are drawn up by the speaker's dais on the district centre square. All around them is a great crowd of relatives and friends to see them off. The tall, broad-chested Cossack, Yakov Zemlyakov, is on the dais:

'I'm a former battery man, a Red partisan. I went right

through the civil war. I've brought up my son. Now he's an artillery man like me, in the ranks of the Red Army. He fought against the White Finns, he was wounded, and now he's fighting the German Fascists. As a first-class artillery man, a gunlayer, I couldn't stand the Fascists' betrayal, and so I've handed in a request to the military commissariat to enrol me as a volunteer in the ranks of the Red Army, in the same regiment as my son, so that we can smash the Fascist beasts together, just as twenty years ago we smashed the White Guard beasts. I want to go and fight as a Communist, and so I ask the party organization to accept me as a candidate.'

Zemlyakov is followed by the young Cossack Roman Vypryazhkin. He says:

'The Finnish White Guards killed my brother. I ask to be enrolled as a volunteer in the ranks of the Red Army and to be sent to the front, to take my brother's place and exact a merciless vengeance for his death.'

An old workman named Pravdenko says:

'I've got two sons in the Red Army. One is in the air force, the other in the infantry. My fatherly command to them is: fight the enemy mercilessly, until he's completely annihilated, in the air and on the ground. But if they have need of support, then I, an old man, will take a rifle in my hand and fight as I did when I was young.'

The ripening winter wheat – thick, tall and juicily green – stands like a wall along the roadside, like young reeds. The rye is taller than a man. The solid bluish ears bend heavily as they swing in the wind.

To avoid our approaching car a horseman turns into the rye and is lost to sight at once: neither horse nor the rider's white shirt is to be seen, only the band of his Cossack cap shows crimson above the green flood, like the head of a thistle in flower.

We stop the car. The horseman comes back on to the road and, pointing to the rye, says:

'Look at the handsome young beauty that's been born; and now Hitler's come along, may he be damned in hell! But he's made a mistake! Oh, he's made a mistake all right! I haven't been home for two days: got anything to smoke, I've run right out of baccy? And tell me, what's the news from the front?'

We tell him the contents of the latest communiqués. Stroking his flaxen whiskers, tinged with grey, he says:

'Our youngsters are fighting like demons, that's clear. But what will it be like when they call on us, the old soldiers who've survived three wars? We'll cut them down right to the navels with which their midwives tied them, the sons of bitches. I tell you, they've made a mistake.'

The Cossack dismounts, squats on his heels and starts smoking, turning his back to the wind, holding the reins in one hand.

'How are things with you in your hamlet?' we ask. 'What do the older Cossacks say about the war?'

'They've got only one thought: to get in the hay and make a proper job of the harvest. But if the Red Army needs us sooner we're ready this moment if need be. The women will manage without us. You know, we've made good tractor and combine drivers out of them.' He winked craftily, and laughed. 'And the Soviet Government isn't dozing, she hasn't got time to doze. Of course life is quieter out here on the steppe, but the Cossacks never did seek a quiet life and never wanted to be buried. In this war we'll go willingly. There's a great anger among the people against that Hitler. Does he find it so sickening to live without war? And where's he trying to get to?'

Our companion smoked for a while without talking, glancing at his peacefully grazing horse. Then he said meditatively:

'I heard about the war on Sunday, and it fair upset me. I can't sleep at all at night, I'm all the time thinking: last year we were plagued with locusts, and this year Hitler's advancing. There's never any satisfaction for the people. And then I think: but what is this Hitler, what is this harmful insect that goes swarming over everything and never gives anyone any peace? But then I remembered the German war, and I had to serve right through it to the end; I remembered how I cut down the enemy. . . . I ended by killing eight with this very hand, and all in attacks. . . .' The Cossack smiled an embarrassed smile, and said in an undertone: 'Now I can talk about it aloud, but in the past I've always felt a bit awkward. . . . I won two George Crosses and three medals. They didn't hang them on me just for nothing, did they? That's just the point. And so I lie awake at night, thinking of that war, and it occurred to me: somewhere a long time ago I read in a paper that Hitler was in the German war too. And then I felt so bitterly upset in my heart that I all but sat up in bed and said aloud: "Why didn't he run into me then, why wasn't he one of the eight?" One swing with my sabre and he'd have been carved in two. My wife asks: "Who are you grieving over?" "Over Hitler," I tell her, "may he be thrice accursed! You sleep, Nastya. It's not anything for you to worry about." '

The Cossack put out the cigarette butt between his fingers and added as he swung himself into the saddle:

'Well, yes, but he'll meet his end, the enemy.' After a pause he turned to me with a stern look as he pulled on the reins: "If you happen to go to Moscow, Alexandrovich, tell them the Don Cossacks of all ages are ready for service. Farewell. I'm hurrying to the hay-mowing section to give the women citizen-esses a hand.'

In a minute the horseman was lost to sight; only the light clumps of dust floating in the wind, flung up by his horse's hoofs from the loamy slope of the ravine, marked his road.

That evening a group of collective farmers gathered on the verandah of the Mokhov village Soviet. The elderly, hollow-cheeked collective farmer Kuznetsov talked calmly, and his enormous work-worn hands lay calmly on his knees.

'. . . I was wounded and taken prisoner. As soon as I was fit they put me to work. They harnessed us up, eight men at a time, to a plough. We ploughed the German land. Then they sent us to the mines. We had to load eight tons of coal at a stint, but with the strength we had we loaded two. If you didn't do your stint you were beaten. They stood you with your face to the wall and beat you on the back of your neck, so that your face struck the wall. Then they put us into a barbed-wire cage. The cage was low, you could only just squat down. Two hours you'd sit, and then they raked you out with a rake, you couldn't crawl out with your own strength.' Kuznetsov looked around his audience with calm eyes, and went on just as calmly: 'Look at me! I'm thin and sickly now, but I still weigh seventy kilos. But in the two and a half years I was their prisoner I didn't weigh forty kilos. That's what they reduced me to.'

Several distinct seconds of silence, then the same calm voice of collective farmer Kuznetsov continues:

'Two of my sons are fighting the German Fascists now. I, too, think the time has come to go and settle accounts. Only, forgive me, citizens, but I won't take them prisoner. I can't.'

There is a profound, troubled silence. Not raising his eyes, still gazing at his quivering, brown hands, and dropping his voice, Kuznetsov adds:

'Of course I ask to be excused, citizens. But they drank my health away to the very bottom. . . . And if my turn comes to go and fight, maybe I will take their soldiers prisoner, but I can't their officers. I can't, and there's nothing more to be said. I had to stand the worst treatment from their officers. And so you must excuse me.' He rose to his feet, huge, gaunt, his eyes unusually bright and youthful with his hatred.

On the second day of the war everybody, from the youngest to the oldest, in the collective farm of Vashchaev hamlet went out to work in the fields. Even men and women who had long since been freed from labour because of their age went out. There were only old men and women working to clean out the threshing floor not far from the hamlet. An aged man, going green with age, was clearing the grass with a spade as he sat with his shaking legs wide apart.

'What are you working sitting down for, grand-dad?'

'I find it difficult to bend my back, so it's easier for me sitting.'

But when one of the elderly women also working there remarked: 'You ought to go home, daddy, we'll manage without you,' the old fellow youthfully raised his colourless eyes to look at her, and answered sternly:

'I've got three grandsons fighting in the war, and I ought to help them any way I can. You're young yet to teach me. When you reach my age, then you can teach. So there!'

Two feelings live in the hearts of the Don Cossacks: love of their native land and hatred for the Fascist usurpers. Their love will live for ever, but the hatred will go on living till the enemy is finally smashed.

A great misfortune will overtake him who aroused this hatred and the cold fury of the people's anger.

1941

On the Cossack Collective Farms

All over the boundless fields of the Don region the harvest is in full swing. Caterpillar tractors are clattering, above the chains of the combine harvesters a fine blue smoke mingles with the rusty whitish dust, the horse-drawn harvesting machines rattle as their wings raise the tall, thick rye. It would seem to be a peaceful picture, but it is not; for over all lies the stern impress of the war. The people and the machines are working differently from in the past – vehemently, tensely. On the district centre squares the golden and sorrel horses, driven in from the droves, tear at the tether-posts; sunburnt young horsemen in faded cavalry caps are riding to the call-up points; and, straightening their backs, the women, binding the sheaves, wave after them and shout: 'Safe return, Cossacks! Beat the snakes to death. Give Budionny a low bow from the Don.'

Carts loaded with grain from the new harvest drag along over the steppe by-roads to the grain collection points. Swaying majestically, enormous wagons, piled high with splendid hay which has not seen rain, as green as an onion, roll by. The Red Army needs everything. And everything is being done for the army. All thoughts are turned to the front. And in all hearts is only one desire: to break the back of the accursed Fascist reptile as quickly as possible.

An elderly collective farm Cossack says with a smile as he husks an ear of wheat in his palms:

'It's not simply that England and other intelligent nations are allied with us; nature itself is for us and against Hitler. Look at the grain this year: it's as good as a fairy tale. The rye has grown as stout as cart shafts, the potatoes are like cart-wheels. The spring wheat, the sunflowers and millet all needed rain, and then, just before the harvest, rain poured down as though to order. Now you can't feast your eyes enough on the spring wheat and the other crops. Everything's coming to our help.'

In the next section of the 'Bolshevik Road' collective farm the combine driver Piotr Zelenkov is driving his machine. The very first hectare of rye yielded 28 centners[1] with a comparatively low moisture content and an insignificant percentage of weed. In some places the yield has risen to between 30 and 35 centners per hectare. Zelenkov's combine discharges its load as it works, and one has to wait some time before it comes to a halt. During a brief rest Zelenkov glances into the corn bin, comes down the ladder on to the stubble field and slips aside for a smoke.

'If you have to go to the front have you trained your replacement?' I ask him.

'Of course.'

'And who will it be?'

'My wife.'

'Can she really take your place?'

Swarthy with sun and dust, Zelenkov smiles. The young woman at the combine steering wheel hangs over the rail and says:

'I'm his wife. At the moment I'm doing the steering, but last year I worked on the combine and earned more than my husband.'

Zelenkov evidently wasn't pleased with what his wife had said, and he took charge of the conversation.

'If the worst comes to the worst she can replace me, of course,' he says reluctantly. 'But we've got another idea: to go to the front together.'

However, Marina Zelenkova is obviously the sort that insists on having the last word. Interrupting her husband, she says:

'We haven't any children; there's no difficulty about our going to fight. And I can drive a tank just as well as my husband, you needn't worry!'

Zelenkov hurries back to the combine. He hasn't time to waste on talking. Out of the 540 hectares of rye on the collective

[1] A hectare equals 2·47 acres; a centner roughly equals a hundredweight.

farm fields, 417 have already been cut by horse-drawn harvesters. And he is hurrying to clear what is left.

In the overwhelming majority of the collective farms in the Rostov area this year only the simpler type of harvesting machines has been used. The Cossacks did not wait for the grain to ripen sufficiently for combines to be used; they set to work to harvest with horse-drawn harvesters, thus saving an enormous quantity of fuel and accelerating the harvesting process. One remark made by a collective farmer is characteristic: 'When we started the collective farms we stopped having to work hard. The Soviet régime saved us from the heaviest work. And now by the evening the youngsters who have to work on the horse-drawn harvesters are complaining that they can't straighten their backs. But that's all eyewash. The tractors did the ploughing for us, the combines did the scything and threshing. All that's fine enough in days of peace, but now the Fascist has started fighting there's no point in looking over our shoulders. We've got to work till our joints crack, and we must save all the fuel we can to send to the Red Army. They need it more there, and they'll use it to such good purpose that the Fascists' joints will crack and turn inside out.' And, as though exchanging ideas with the old man, Vasily Soldatov, a member of the collective farm named after the twenty-six Baku Commissars, and a man who has twice beaten the rate set for stacking the hay, comes down from the rick and remarks as he squeezes the sweat out of his shirt: 'Our enemy's brutal and obstinate, so we, too, must work brutally and obstinately. As for the rate, what of it? We've got to exceed the rate here, and when we go off to the front we'll beat the enemy without setting any rates.'

In all the collective farms I have visited there is excellent labour discipline, a high consciousness of civic duty. Children and old men are at work in the fields, and even those who had a minimal number of labour days to their credit last year are working. All without exception are working with great enthusiasm, not sparing their strength. After listening to the restrained praise of one of the district officials the brigadier of the third brigade of the 'Bolshevik Road' collective farm, Vasily Tselikov, answered:

'We simply can't work badly. The way I see it is that at the

165

moment we're defending our country with our labour. But if necessary we'll defend it with guns. And besides, how can we work badly when almost every house has a man fighting in the Red Army? For instance, I've got two sons, and they're both at the front; Alexei is in the artillery, Nikolai is in the tanks. And although I'm an old man, I've enrolled in the home guard. In the last war I was shot through the belly on the German front. That German bullet robbed me of a lot of health, but I can still work. At the moment my sons are dealing with the enemy; but if necessary I'll stand in the ranks with them!'

When he heard that I would be writing for the *Red Star*[1] he added animatedly:

'Write through the *Red Star* to my boys and all the fighters who're at the front that the rear won't let them down. Tell them not to let the Fascists pass, tell them to drive them into their graves, so that our land may become their dark tomb.'

In the administration office of the 'Road to Socialism' collective farm one book-keeper, no longer young, is at work. The chairman is out in the fields. There is not another soul in the village. All the people are in the field brigades, mowing, cleaning the threshing floors, loading the grain. Looking up from his papers for a moment, the book-keeper says:

'My son's on the western front. He's been three years in the service as a gunner. I used sometimes to write to him and ask: "Let me know what gun you're in charge of." He answered: "I'm alive and well; my greetings to the family. But as for the type of gun, there's no point in inquiring, father; it's none of your business." ' The book-keeper smiles and says with a satisfied air: 'So he knows his duty. I, too, was on all the fronts during the civil war. I fought in the north, and I fought the Basmachy brigands, and whoever else we had to smash. And now I'm in the home guard.' After a moment he added: 'In our hamlet there are about a hundred in the home guard. But all the same, it's an extraordinary war. There are a devil of a lot of young people still at home. When we draw up our company, as well as us older men you'll see lots of youngsters old enough to man a gun. They're not lads, they're stallions! They've signed on as volunteers, but for some reason they

[1] The Red Army newspaper. (Tr.)

166

haven't been called up yet. So we must have an enormous reserve of strength. It's quite pleasant to think of.'

The second brigade of this collective farm is working with horse-drawn mowing machines. Two pairs of oxen are harnessed to each mower, the wings of the mower are raised to their highest level; but it is difficult to fork the corn off the platform, so high and thick is the rye. The women drivers urge on the oxen zealously; the very young Cossacks forking the corn off the platforms don't have time to wipe away the sweat pouring into their eyes. During a momentary halt I go up to them and ask why they're driving the oxen almost at a trot. One of the lads answers:

'We're making the oxen work; nothing will happen to them, and it's easier to throw off the corn when we're moving fast. We'll get in the harvest, then we'll go off to the front. But the women will find it rather hard to deal with grain like this.' And at once the question follows: 'When will they be taking us into the army? They've taken others of my age, but they've left me for some reason. I'm quite upset about it. Am I any worse than the others?'

This collective farmer's name is Pokusayev. He is the son of the local smith, and a healthy, broad-chested lad. He has done his service in the Red Army artillery. From talks with the others it comes out that one was recently a tank driver, another was in the artillery, in a howitzer battery, a third was an A.A. gunner, a fourth a cavalry man in one of our famous divisions. Every one of them a picked lad, young, strong, healthy. And their desire to go and fight an enemy drunk with blood and cheap successes is understandable. That is the desire of the young Don Cossacks, yesterday's and tomorrow's soldiers in the great Red Army. It is the desire of those whose forebears over the centuries shed their blood on the frontiers of Russia, their native country, defending it against innumerable enemies.

And now I recall the words of eighty-three-year-old Isaiah Markovich Yevlantiev, who is guarding the collective farm threshing floor. It is a dark July night. Shooting stars in the black sky. And that quiet, aged voice:

'My grandfather fought against Napoleon, and he used to

tell me stories about it when I was a boy. Before Napoleon came to make war on us, one fine day he gathered his Murats and generals in the open field and said: "I'm thinking of conquering Russia. What have you to say to that, gentlemen?" And they all said with one voice: "That's quite impossible, Your Imperial Majesty; it's a very powerful State, we'll never conquer it." Napoleon pointed to the sky, and asked: "Do you see a star in the sky?" "No," they said. "It isn't possible to see the stars in daylight." "But I see it," he says. "It foretells our victory." So he set his army against us. He entered by wide gates, but he went out through narrow ones; he had to force his way through at a gallop. And our soldiers accompanied him right to his capital, to Paris. I think with my old mind that this German commander-in-chief has also seen a stupid star like that; and when the time comes for him to go out, the gates will be made narrow for him, oh, very narrow! Will he gallop through them, or not? God grant that he doesn't! So that others from now on and for ever will not try again!'

1941

An Infamy

A communiqué from our army in the field reports: 'Close to the village of Yelnia stubborn fighting developed. The Fascists built fortifications in front of the houses, camouflaged them and continued to return our fire for some time. But when our forces went over to the offensive the Fascists drove all the women and children out of the village and distributed them in front of their trenches.'

This was done by soldiers of Hitler's army, by men whose valour and nobility are constantly being extolled by the Fascist radio. From such 'nobility' rises the rotting, sickening stink of corruption. And involuntarily one thinks: if the Nazi soldiers who committed this shameful deed at Yelnia survive, how will they be able to look into the eyes of their mothers, their wives and sisters, without a feeling of shame?

Evidently Fascist propaganda has done its job properly, eliminating all human feelings from the souls of the Hitlerite soldiers, turning living people into automata carrying out inhuman and savage tasks.

I don't know what the incident at Yelnia will be called in Goebbels's language; military enterprise perhaps, or a demonstration of German ingenuity. But in the languages of all the civilized nations of the world such conduct, dishonouring to a soldier, has always been, and always will be, called infamy. And all who learn of this latest manifestation of Fascist infamy will have a feeling of burning shame for the German people, and loathing and hatred for him who in wartime, forgetting all shame, hid behind the backs of peaceable, unarmed inhabitants.

The peoples of the Soviet Union and their Red Army are keeping an account of the evil-doings of the German Fascists.

And there will be but one answer: the Fascists will pay with much blood for the blood they have shed of our people, and with blood will they have to settle accounts for their own dishonour.

1941

Prisoners of War

Their battalion was loaded into lorries in Paris and transferred to the East. They took with them the articles they had looted in France: French wine and French cars.

From Minsk to the front line they marched on foot, for they had to leave their lorries behind in Minsk owing to the shortage of petrol. Drunk with the victories of the German armies, and also with French wine, they moved along the dusty roads of Belorussia with their sleeves rolled up, their collars unbuttoned. Their steel helmets dangled from their belts; their bare, sweaty heads were dried by the kindly sun and warm breezes of alien Russia. They still had wine in their flasks, and the soldiers marched bravely through the burnt-out Soviet villages and sang their ribald regimental song of how the beautiful French girl, Jeanne, had seen real soldiers for the first time, and had had the satisfaction of knowing real men, only when the Germans entered Paris.

But then, by day and by night, on the march and in bivouac, they began to be harried by partisans. In six days the one battalion lost some forty men killed and wounded. A motorcyclist sent back to staff headquarters disappeared. Six soldiers and one lance-corporal disappeared. They set out for a local village to obtain some food for the company and did not return. The men of the battalion sang less and less about the beautiful Jeanne who was so satisfied with the Germans. Here the people were dissatisfied with the Germans. When the battalion entered a ruined village the inhabitants fled and hid in the forest, and those they found at home were sullen and stared down at the ground, to conceal from the German soldiers the hatred that burned in their eyes. In the chance intercepted glances of the men and women there was more hatred than fear. No, this was not France.

If one can believe him, Lance-Corporal Fritz Berkmann

171

did not take any part in the massacre of the civilian population. He considers himself a decent, cultured man, and, of course, he is a resolute opponent of unnecessary harshness. And when one day drunken soldiers of his company, laughing and joking, dragged a young woman collective farmer into a shed, he went out of the yard so as not to hear her screams. The woman was young and strong. She put up a bitter resistance, as the result of which one soldier lost an eye. But the others dealt with her. After they had raped her, the blinded soldier finished her off.

When Lance-Corporal Berkmann heard of this he was terribly upset. He himself could never have committed such a beastly deed at any price. He had a wife and two children in Nuremburg, and he wouldn't like anything of that sort to happen to his wife. But he could not be held responsible for the activities of the beasts who, unfortunately, were in the German Army. When he reported what had happened, his lieutenant shrugged his shoulders – war is war – and ordered Berkmann not to bother him with trifles.

Straight from the march the battalion was flung into a battle. For twenty-six days the soldiers did not leave the trenches. In Berkmann's company, out of one hundred and seventy men only thirty-eight were left. The soldiers were depressed by their enormous losses. No, this wasn't the sort of war against the Russians they had envisaged as they rode out of France bawling their songs. The officers had told them they would march through Russia as easily as a knife passes through butter. It had all proved vainglorious boasting, and many of the officers who had talked like that now had nothing to say: truly, the bullets of the Russian snipers and the shards of Russian shells passed through their bodies with the same ease as a knife passes through butter.

Berkmann was taken prisoner this morning, during our attack. Before he was brought into our dug-out Red Army men bandaged his eyes tightly.

'Are you going to shoot me?' he asked in a quivering voice.

But the Red Army men didn't know German, and made no answer to his question.

His legs giving way beneath him with fear, Berkmann came

into the dug-out. The bandage was removed from his eyes. When he saw men sitting peaceably round a table he sighed hoarsely, with all his heart, and with such relief that I was quite upset.

'I thought I was being taken out to be shot,' he stammered his explanation of his involuntary sigh. He stood at once to attention.

He was invited to sit down. He dropped on to a chair, putting his hands on his knees.

And there he sits in front of us, this *Landknecht* of Nazi Germany, answering our questions in detail.

He still has not recovered from his agitation. His cheek is twitching with a nervous tic, the hands on his knees are trembling. With all his strength he is trying to suppress his agitation and to conceal his trembling; but he is not very successful. Only after he has avidly smoked the cigarette he is offered does he begin to regain his balance.

He has fair curly hair and wide-set blue eyes, not very intelligent. He is indubitably an Aryan, is badly shaken up by the war and very hungry. Their daily ration consisted of three cigarettes, a little bread and half a mess-tin of hot food. It wasn't always possible to bring up the hot food, and they were desperately hungry.

What does he think about the outcome of the war with Soviet Russia? He regards it as a hopeless enterprise. The Führer made a mistake in attacking Russia. Russia is a very large mouthful, which may choke poor Germany. Here he, Lance-Corporal Berkmann, has the opportunity to express his opinion freely, something he could never do in his own unit, for there are secret members of the Nazi party who spy on their own soldiers. Any unguarded remark brings you before a rifle muzzle. He personally thinks they should have completely finished off England, taken her colonies and called it a day.

His impressions of the Soviet territory they have occupied can be summed up in three words: shortage of produce. Everything the population had was consumed by the leading German forces. To find a chicken is bliss. He speaks almost with hatred of the German tank forces and mobile columns.

'Those cattle clear up everything; where they've been you follow as if going through a desert.'

It is difficult to talk with Lance-Corporal Berkmann. Listening to the cynical remarks of this hysterically garrulous and stupid pillager in soldier's uniform, one finds it growing more and more stifling in the dug-out, one wants to get out into the fresh air. We cut the conversation short.

In conclusion, standing up and drawing himself up to attention, he tells of how two hours ago, during the interrogation, he honestly informed the Soviet commander of the position and numerical strength of his battalion, the staff and their reserve of military stores. He has told all he knows, since he is a convinced opponent of war with Russia. On checking, the information he has supplied will be completely confirmed, so he asks us to allow him to inform his wife that he is a prisoner, and, if this is possible, to give him some more food, as the last time he had any was seven hours ago.

A youngster, beardless, twenty years of age. Sleekly brushed hair, blue blotches on his cheeks and thievishly shifty eyes. A member of the German National Socialist Party. A tank man. He has been in France, Yugoslavia and Greece. Yesterday during the battle his tank was blown up by a Red Army man with a bunch of hand grenades. Jumping out of his tank, he returned the fire. Wounded by four bullets . . . light wounds. Occasionally he frowns with the pain, but he bears himself with insolent, exaggerated courage. He does not raise his eyes when answering questions. Certain questions he flatly refuses to answer; but, on the other hand, he talks volubly, using phrases learnt by heart, about the superiority of the German nation, the inferiority of the French, English and Slavonic nations. No, he is not a man, but a poorly cooked dumpling with an evil-smelling stuffing. Not a single thought of his own, no spiritual or intellectual interests. We ask him whether he knows Pushkin, or Shakespeare. He knits his brows, thinks, then asks:

'Who are they?' And, when he is told, he twists his thin lips into a contemptuous smile and says: 'I don't know them, and I don't want to. I don't feel any necessity to.'

174

He is convinced that Germany will win. With dull, idiotic obstinacy he asserts:

'By the winter our army will have settled with you, and then all our strength will be hurled against England. England must perish.'

'But supposing Russia and England settle with Germany?'

'That's impossible. The Führer has said that we shall conquer,' the prisoner answers, staring down at his feet. He answers like a stupid pupil who has learnt his lesson off by heart and doesn't bother his mind with unnecessary reflections.

There is something false, something incredibly hideous in the features of this youngster; and only one of his remarks carries the ring of sincerity:

'I'm sorry my military career is ended . . . !'

Hopelessly perverted by Nazi propaganda, this young ruffian has not ceased killing. He has only just acquired the taste for killing, he hasn't yet smelt blood to the full, but now he is a prisoner. And now he sits in front of us, rendered harmless once for all, and stares with the eyes of an envenomed, blood-thirsty polecat, and his nostrils dilate with his blind hatred for us.

Six German prisoners of war escorted by a Red Army man came out of the tent and squatted down on the ground, which was littered with pine needles. They had only just been brought in after being taken prisoner. Their uniforms are patched and filthy, one of them has his boot sole tied on with wire. They haven't had a wash for six days. Our artillery had deprived them of that possibility. Their faces are gloomy, covered with a layer of dried mud. Sitting in the trenches they have grown lousy, and now they scratch themselves without constraint, combing their heads with their black fingers. Only one of them, a handsome, black-haired lad, smiles with satisfaction and, turning to me, says:

'The war's all over for me. I'm happy to have been taken prisoner so conveniently.'

They are brought hot borsch in billy cans.

They fling themselves like animals on the food and, burning themselves, guzzling, hardly stopping to chew, they gulp it

175

down hurriedly, greedily. Two of them haven't brought spoons with them. They don't wait for spoons to be brought, they plunge their filthy fingers into the billy cans, fish out the solid pieces of food and transfer them to their mouths, throwing back their heads and screwing up their eyes blissfully.

When they have had enough they get up, heavy and sleepy. Suppressing a belch, a stocky lance-corporal says:

'Thank you. My very grateful thanks. We can't remember the last time we ate so well.'

The interpreter says a seventh prisoner has refused food and is sitting in the tent. When we enter an elderly German soldier, long unshaven and very thin, gets up and draws his large horny hands down his trouser seams. We ask why he is refusing to eat.

In a voice quivering with emotion the soldier says:

'I'm a peasant. I was mobilized in July. In two months of war I've seen enough of the destruction carried out by our army, the abandoned fields, and all we've done here in the East. I couldn't sleep, and food sticks in my throat. I know we've ruined almost all Europe just like this, and I know Germany will have to pay dearly for it. And not only that dog Hitler but all the German nation will have to pay. Do you understand me?'

He turns away and is a long time silent. Well, it is a good meditation. And the sooner the German soldiers realize their heavy responsibility and the inevitability of the settlement, the closer will be the victory of democracy over rabid Nazism.

1941

In the South

The sun rises over the sombrely smoking pyramid of the slag heap. The lilac shadows on the snow lighten with extraordinary speed; and then the roofs of the miners' small cottages, the window-panes decorated with frost, the hoar-frosted branches of the roadside maples, and the distant azure, snowy crests of the rises, suddenly flare up with a blinding rosy flame beneath the sun, and the glitter of the road, polished smooth by sledge runners, grows even more unbearable.

From east to west along the broad highway black columns of people are moving. A few men in the last rows of one of the columns slow down, twist themselves home-made cigarettes as they walk and light up. My companion asks:

'Who are all these people? Are they going out to dig defence works?'

Taking a pleasant draw from his home-grown tobacco, a stocky, broad-shouldered man in a greasy, padded coat answers:

'We're the masters of the Don Basin, that's who we are, and we're going to put in order the mines that have been blown up and flooded. Now d'you see?'

They run to overtake the column, and once more in the frosty air their steps blend with the thudding, regular tread of the hundreds of these true masters of the Don Basin on their way to reopen their ruined mines.

There are old men, elderly miners and juveniles in the ranks. And while the bowed, middle-aged master returning to start production seems to personify the past of the Don Basin, these old miners and adolescents represent its present and future. But you will not see the flower of the mining youth among these marchers: the young and strong are far away, in the west; in the Provalov division, in innumerable branches of the Red Army they are fighting to liberate their native Don Basin, they are winning the victory of their great native country.

177

The Italian heavy guns roll thunderously. They are answered by our artillery. The battle has not quite died out throughout the night, and it is renewed with fresh strength in the morning. The German and Italian forces in the Don Basin are resisting with the fury of desperation. They find it hard to abandon the warm huts, to part from the rich fuel of the inhabited centres and to flee into the snowy steppe, where the ground breeze hisses ominously and a wild wind burns them with fire, penetrating to their very bones.

But all the same, they are having to flee. Under the blows of our troops they are changing their quarters more and more frequently, and are hurriedly shifting westwards, abandoning guns and equipment along the roads in their flight.

On the southern front, perhaps more than on any other, one gets a broad idea of the varied nature and the motley languages of the Fascist Army. What nation isn't represented among the prisoners taken by our forces? Germans, Italians and Rumanians are predominant in the muddy scum of disarmed ruffians who only recently were torturing the peaceable population of the Ukraine, but Hungarians and Finns are also to be found. Here we really have:

> . . . *a mixture of clothing and features,*
> *Of tribes and tongues and conditions;*
> *From huts, from cells and dark places*
> *They have come running for the plunder.* . . .

Truly, it is plunder and pillage that have brought together this band of beasts and gallows-birds, who trade under the black banner with its bow-legged Fascist swastika. It is about these pillagers, incendiaries and murderers, who with sombre misanthropy have transformed our flourishing regions into a 'zone of wilderness', that Pushkin wrote in the words:

> *Danger, blood, depravity, trickery*
> *Are the bonds of this terrible family;*
> *These are they who with stony soul*
> *Have surpassed all the bounds of criminality,*
> *Who slaughter cold-bloodedly*
> *The widow and the wretched orphan,*

And who find the children's groans amusing;
Those who neither forgive nor spare,
To whom murder is a cause of merriment,
As to a youth is his love assignation.

When taken prisoner their outward features change strikingly. Here they are, crowded in a spacious room, bristling with cold and blowing on their chilly hands. Their unshaven faces are dirty, and look bored; their eyes express such a sadness you might think they were human. From their long unwashed bodies and greasy uniforms rises the sour stench of dogs. The bedraggled cock's feathers on the hats of the Italian Bersaglieri droop miserably. It is as though the wind had blown all the recent polish and insolent self-assurance clean away from these Fascists, lousy with their stay in the trenches. An Italian officer wearing woollen stockings taken from some collective farm woman humbly holds out his hand for a cigarette, and burbles something about not having had a smoke for fifty days.

That is what they look like now. But let us hand over to someone who has seen them in different circumstances. The old collective farmer Kolisnichenko, who recently escaped from Fascist imprisonment, fingers the collar of his old shirt again and again, as though that loose collar were choking him, as he slowly tells us:

'. . . Late in the afternoon some of their motor-cyclists drove through the village. They were followed by six tanks, and behind them came infantry in trucks and on foot. Towards nightfall some special detachment halted for the night; black lightning flashes were painted on the side of each helmet, and every one of them looked like a devil.

'Then began something I can only recall with bitterness and with a feeling of sickness. They drove our girls into the school; some of them they dragged straight through the snow. They made a mock of them as long as they felt like it, and then they killed three of them: Martha Solokhina, Dunia Filipenko and a young married woman from a neighbouring settlement. They killed them in the school, dragged them into the yard and piled them criss-cross one on another just below the verandah.

'All night they went raging through the village, slaughtering

179

fowls and cattle, forcing the women to cook for them, rummaging through the chests, the store-rooms. It was just like the time when we had a fire in the village. The cattle were bellowing, the dogs howling, the girls wailing like the dead. The noise was so fearful it was terrible to go out into the yard, I give you my word.

'Towards morning they quietened down. At dawn I went out through the wicket gate. I looked and saw my neighbour, Trofim Ivanovich Bidiuzhny, lying dead by the well, an overturned bucket beside him. They'd killed him because he went out in the night to fetch water, and according to their laws peaceful inhabitants weren't allowed to go outside even to piss. During the morning they shot another, a boy twelve years old. He went up to one of their motor-cycles to have a look at it – boys are always interested in such things – and a Fascist took aim from a verandah with a revolver, and killed him. They wouldn't give permission to bury the dead. His mother had to see her little son lying. She looked through the window, she looked and dropped as though dead. Her folk brought her round by throwing water over her. I saw him, too, when we were all driven out to attend a meeting. I went past him and saw him. . . . There the boy was lying, all huddled and frozen to the ground. The girls were lying outside the school; their skirts were tied over their heads with telephone wire, their legs were all bruised. Anyone who needed to go past the school went a long way round. We gathered up the dead only when this force had gone.'

The old man abstractedly took the cigarette we offered him, turned it over and over in his hands and, after a brief pause, went on with his story:

'They quartered four men in my hut. The very first day they slaughtered a sow in young, and two sheep. Some they ate on the spot, the rest they took away with them. And they took the sheepskins too. During the morning they started rummaging through the chests and store-rooms. Whatever they fancied they took. They carried off a lot of things with them, and on the last day they even took my felt boots. They were all dressed to go, their engines were running, when suddenly one of them, a tall fellow with badges on his sleeve,

180

pointed to my felt boots and waved his hand: 'Take them off!'
I was sorry to part with my last pair of boots: I began pleading
with him; but the son of a bitch went white with rage, snatched
up a rifle, put the bayonet point against my throat and roared
something or other. My old woman was all in tears, and she
shouts at me:

' "Take them off! Take them off quick, or he'll kill you!"

'But I was afraid; I was silent, and couldn't bend down.
All I could think of was: "Well, this is the end of me." The
Fascist kicked me in the belly, I fell back on the bench, hardly
able to breathe. My mouth was gaping, but I couldn't get any
breath, everything went black before my eyes. My old woman
ran across to me, and she pulled off my felt boots as nimbly
as if she were a young woman, and held them out to the Fascist.
He was about to aim at me again, to plunge the bayonet in me.
But he saw the boots in my wife's hands, and for some reason
had mercy on me. He took the boots, spat in my face and began
to put them on. Three others stood at the door, laughing. The
tall fellow put on my felt boots, put his own boots into a bag,
smiled unpleasantly at the corners of his mouth and was the
first to go out.

'So that lot went off, but a little later another force entered
the village. And they all behaved the same way, and in a few
days our village was stripped bare, peeled like a boiled egg.'

'A fine army!' a young, freckled, and cheerful-looking lieutenant who was present exclaimed.

'They haven't any army!' the old man said sternly. 'Maybe
they did have earlier on, but not now. I haven't seen any.
I myself served in the army; I fought in the Japanese war,
and against the fathers of these Germans; I know army discipline, but I've never seen anything like this, if you don't
mind my saying so.

'Were soldiers ever allowed to pillage and to drag their
sacks of plunder away with them in the old days? There's
no point in denying it, we, too, took food; but we didn't touch
babies' napkins, we didn't pull off the boots and clothing of
old men and women, we didn't fight little children, we didn't
execute women. But today they can do all this without being
restrained. Everything is allowed them, whatever comes into

their heads to do they do. And again, an army ought to be dressed in its proper uniform. But how are this lot dressed? One is wearing a greatcoat, another a sheepskin jerkin taken off my neighbour, a third has an ordinary woman's coat of grey cloth over his uniform. Of course they're all armed; but then the highwaymen who used to lie in wait on the roads also had arms.

'And so we had regular exchanges of lodgers in my hut. One day one lot, the next day another, and all from different countries. One would say, "I'm a Pole," another, "I'm a Hungarian," while a third would say nothing. But I could see by his eyes and his stealthy behaviour he was obviously .a Nazi. Well, I didn't believe what they said of themselves. "You're lying," I thought, "you damned lot! You're not Poles, you're not Hungarians. If you were a Pole you'd be fighting for your Poland, a Hungarian for your Hungarian land. But as it is you're a sort of filthy fungus growing on a dung-heap, you all breathe out the one filthy air."

'One day one of their non-commissioned officers came into my hut and said something swiftly to a soldier who called himself a Hungarian. I could see he didn't understand a word; he shrugged his shoulders, threw out his hands, and his eyes had an absolutely stupid look. Then the Hungarian began to chatter away in his own language, and the non-com drew himself up and turned angry, and even went red in the face.

'They stood almost brow to brow, like a couple of sheep; each of them gabbling away and neither understanding the other. They haven't a common language between them. But when it comes to pillage they've all got the same language: bread, milk, eggs, potatoes, "hand over", "*kaput*", they can all say. And every one of them threatens death with his bayonet or rattles a box of matches and says he'll burn the place down. And you call them an army! What sort of an army is it when it looks as if they've all been let out of the same prison?'

Outside, the night was frosty. The coal burned brightly in the stove. The old man took down a shabby sheepskin jacket from the bedhead, and grunting and groaning, began putting it on. Standing with one arm thrust into a sleeve, he repeated obstinately:

'They haven't got an army, I tell you straight!'

Turning to him respectfully, the lieutenant said:

'Of course, you're right, daddy; but they, too, have an idea for which they're fighting.'

The old man froze still for a second, with the sheepskin stretched over his arms. But then he asked sternly, as though recovering from his astonishment:

'What sort of idea? They haven't any ideas; the very word doesn't suit them.'

'But they have got one,' the lieutenant declared, hiding a barely perceptible twinkle in his eyes.

The old man sat down in the bed and stared without speaking into the lieutenant's face, knitting his ruddy brows with their tinge of grey. His voice had a note of sarcastic officialdom as he asked:

'Then explain to me, comrade commander, just what their idea is. You see, I'm not well educated, and maybe I don't understand the word properly.'

'Don't be angry, daddy,' the lieutenant said in a conciliatory tone. 'Their ideas are just exactly as you've said. Some five days ago we surrounded a camp of theirs; they had over thirty carts with them. They lay down around the carts, firing. They were done for, they couldn't get away, but they wouldn't surrender. Beside me lay a young soldier who had only recently joined the force as part of our reinforcements. He sees them defending themselves desperately and he says to me: "You can tell they're Fascists with ideas, comrade lieutenant. Look, they refuse to give in." "Okay," I said, "we'll beat them, and then we'll see what sort of ideas they've got."

'Well, we beat them as I had said, killed them all off to the last man and started examining their bundles and bales. This group was on its way to the rear, and we all know what they send to the rear, apart from their wounded. We slit up one bale, and it was full of children's boots, lengths of cloth and other material, women's jackets, both cloth and fur, wheat in bags, goloshes and other odds and ends. The second bale we opened contained just the same sort of things. I called over the soldier who had suspected the Nazis of having ideas, and I said: "D'you see what they had in those bales?" "Yes." "Well, then," I said, "there's all the ideas they fought for. Their ideas are all packed in sacks, and their lining is of cloth. Get that?" "I get it now," the Red Army man said with a laugh.'

The old man had listened attentively to the lieutenant; and now he said with an unconcealed tone of superiority in his voice:

'That's not the way to talk, my son, though you are an officer. You don't know what an idea is, so I'll explain it to you. The chairman of our collective farm, Ivan Ivanovich Cherepitsa, used to say: "Citizens, I've got an idea to build a dam across the Dry Ravine and to rear carp in the pond." All the village got down to the work, and even before the war we'd carried a ton and half of carp to the market, without counting what we ate ourselves.

'Or he'd say: "Well, collective farm citizens, what do you think of the idea of building a turbine-driven mill?" And in due course the mill would be ready, and even neighbouring collective farms brought us their grain to be ground. The same thing happened with the idea of an apiary, and with the Silesian sheep, and quite a lot of other things on our farm.

'So now do you understand what the word "idea" means? My dear man, it means something which brings the people benefit. But you tie up this good word to pillage. Pillage, that's just called pillage. Do the Fascists pillage? And do they do it a lot? That means the word "idea" can't be applied to them, and to use it when talking about Fascists isn't right, it only gets fouled by those sons of bitches. You're young men, and there are some things you still don't understand in this life. I tell you that straight!'

The enemy are still holding out desperately, they are even talking of a spring offensive. But when the spring comes the enemy won't be the same Nazis who trod our soil last year. Under the crushing blows of the Red Army they have moulted, and moulted without hope of recovery. The prisoner Wilhelm Wojzik, a lance-corporal of the third regiment of the 160th rifle battalion of the 60th motorized division, says:

'The words "get back home" and "back to Germany" have become the one password of all the soldiers.'

This lance-corporal, who has some gift of observation, was asked about the quality of the reserves being sent to his battalion. He declared: 'A new element has appeared in the soldiers of the reinforcements: they're always silent and they smoke an awful lot.'

An interesting element! Let them try waging an offensive with reserves like that!

1942

A Lesson in Hatred

In a war trees are like human beings, they each have their destiny. I have seen an enormous expanse of forest cut down by the fire of our artillery. Recently Germans driven out of a certain village consolidated their forces in this forest; they planned to hold out here, but death scythed them down together with the trees. The dead German soldiers lay under the over-thrown pine trunks; their bodies, torn to shreds, were rotting in the green bracken; and the resinous scent of the pines splintered by shells could not overcome the horribly sickly, pungent smell of decomposing bodies. It seemed as though even the earth was exuding the stench of the grave with the harsh burnt edges of its shell craters.

Death ruled majestically and silently over a glade which had been created and ploughed by our shells; yet right in the very middle of the glade stood one birch tree, miraculously spared. The wind swayed the shattered stumps of its branches and rustled among the glossy, sticky young leaves.

We had to pass through this glade. A Red Army liaison man who was walking in front of me touched the birch trunk gently with his hand, and asked in genuine, kindly amazement:

'But how did you manage to escape, my dear?'

A pine perishes when struck by a shell, it falls as though scythed down; and only a crown with its needles, streaming with resin, is left lying in the place of slaughter. But an oak meets death in a different manner.

In the late winter a German shell dropped into the trunk of an old oak growing on the bank of some nameless stream. The ragged, yawning gash withered half the tree; but in the spring the other half, which had been bent down to the water by the explosion, came wildly to life and was covered with fresh foliage. And doubtless to this very day the lower branches of that mutilated oak are bathing in the flowing water, while the higher branches still avidly stretch their stiff, serrated leaves up to the sun.

Lieutenant Gerasimov, a tall man with a slight stoop, his broad shoulders hunched high, making him look like a kite, sat at the entrance to his dug-out and gave us circumstantial details of today's battle, an enemy tank attack which his battalion had successfully repulsed.

The lieutenant's lean face was calm, almost dispassionate; his inflamed eyes were screwed up wearily. He talked in a cracked bass voice, from time to time interlocking his large, gnarled fingers; and this gesture, so eloquently conveying a speechless sorrow or a deep, oppressive meditation, was strangely at variance with his powerful figure and his energetic, masculine face.

But suddenly he fell silent, and momentarily his face was transformed: the swarthy cheeks turned pale, and under the cheekbones the fleshy muscles rose and fell, while the fixed, staring eyes blazed with such unquenchable, savage hatred that I involuntarily turned to follow his gaze. I saw three German prisoners coming through the forest from the direction of our front line, and behind them a Red Army escort, in a summer tunic faded almost white with the sun; his peaked cap was thrust to the back of his head.

The Red Army man was walking slowly. A rifle swung measuredly in his hands, its bayonet point glittered in the sunlight. And the German prisoners advanced just as slowly, reluctantly shifting their feet, which were shod in muddy ankle-length boots.

The German who led the way – an elderly man with sunken cheeks thickly overgrown with chestnut scrub – drew level with our dug-out; as he passed he cast a wolfish glance towards us, then turned away, adjusting the helmet hanging from his belt. And then Lieutenant Gerasimov sprang violently to his feet and shouted after the Red Army man in a sharp, piercing voice:

'What are you doing: taking them for a stroll? Get a move on! Take them along faster, I tell you!'

He seemed about to shout something more; but he choked

187

with agitation and, turning sharply, ran down the steps into the dug-out. In response to my astonished look, the Political Instructor who had been present at our conversation said in an undertone:

'You can't do anything about it; it's just his nerves. He was taken prisoner by the Germans: didn't you know? Have a talk with him when you get a chance. He had some pretty bad experiences at their hands, and ever since then he just can't stand the sight of living Nazis: I said "living ones". He can look at dead ones, I'd say it even gives him satisfaction. But when he sees prisoners he either covers his eyes and sits pale and sweating or he turns away and goes off somewhere.' The Political Instructor shifted closer to me and dropped his voice to a whisper: 'I've had to go into an attack twice with him; he's got the strength of a horse, and you should see what he does. . . . I've seen some sights in my time, but the way he uses his bayonet and butt . . . you know, it's fearful to see!'

During the night the German artillery kept up a disturbing fire. Methodically, at equal intervals of time. We heard the sound of gunfire in the distance, and a few seconds later we heard the steely scream of the shell pass over our heads, high in the starry sky; the howl rose and then died away, and somewhere behind us, in the direction of the road along which trucks carrying military supplies up to our front line were moving in dense columns, a flame flew up in a yellow flash of sheet lightning, and there was a thunderous explosion.

In the intervals between the shells, when quiet was restored in the forest, one could hear the thin buzz of mosquitoes; and frogs, disturbed by the firing, timorously called to one another in the neighbouring marsh.

We lay under a hazel bush, and Lieutenant Gerasimov, keeping the mosquitoes off with a broken twig, unhurriedly told me his story. I give it exactly as I remember it.

'Up to the war I worked as an engineer in one of the factories in Western Siberia. I was called up into the army on July 9th last year. I have a family: my wife, two boys and my father, who was wounded and invalided out in the last war. Well, at the parting, as you would expect, my wife cried, and as a

send-off she said: "Defend our homeland and us with all your
strength. If necessary give your life, so long as we gain the
victory." I remember I laughed at the time, and told her:
"What are you, my wife or the family propagandist? I'm quite
grown up, you know; and as for victory, we'll wring it from the
Fascists as we wring their throats, never fear."

'My father, of course, was stronger; but he, too, couldn't
see me off without his parting instructions: "Remember,
Victor," he says, "the name of Gerasimov is no ordinary one.
You're a worker by heredity: your great-grandfather worked
for Stroganov; our family has made iron for the country for
hundreds of years, and you see to it that you're iron in this war.
The government is yours, it kept you as a commander in
reserve until the war; and you must hit the enemy hard."

' "That will be done, father."

'On my way to the station I dropped into the party district
committee office. Our secretary was a very dry, judicial sort
of fellow. And I was thinking, if my wife and father gave me a
lecture for the road, our secretary won't let me go scot free,
he'll make a little speech half an hour long, no doubt of that!
But it was just the reverse. "Sit down, Gerasimov," he said
to me. "Before you set out we'll sit for a minute or two, as is
our custom."

'So I sat with him for a little while; we were silent. Then he
got up, and I noticed his spectacles seemed to be misted. Well,
I thought, what miracles we have today! But he says: "It's
all quite clear and comprehensible, comrade Gerasimov. I
remember you when you were so high, lop-eared, when you
were wearing a Young Pioneer's neckerchief. I remember you
later as a Young Communist, and I've known you as a Communist for the past ten years. Go and beat the reptiles mercilessly!
The party organization relies on you." Then for the first time
in my life I and the secretary kissed each other, and, damn
it all, I realized that he wasn't at all the dry old stick I'd thought
him.

'And then my wife turned quite merry and bright. You
know yourself it isn't at all cheerful for any wife to have to see
her husband off to the front; and of course my wife lost control
of herself a bit in her sorrow. She tried again and again to say

[Handwritten marginal note:] STALIN EVENTUALLY COULD SEND YOU ALL to SIBERIA to NOT + DIE IN PRISEN CAMPS POOR FOOLS

something important, but she had a draught blowing through her head, and it blew all her thoughts away. And then the train started, and she walked along at the side of my carriage, keeping tight hold of my hand and saying hurriedly:

' "Now look, Victor: take care of yourself, don't catch cold there at the front." "Drop it!" I said. "Drop it, Nadia! I shan't catch cold whatever happens. The climate there is good and even very mild." It was painful for me to part from her, and yet I felt brighter because of my wife's dear, stupid words, and I grew angry with the Germans. "Well," I thought, "they've attacked us, the perfidious neighbours. Now hold on! We'll pin you down at the first chance we get." '

Gerasimov was silent for some minutes, listening to the exchange of machine-gun fire which had started up in the front lines. Then, when it stopped, as abruptly as it had begun, he went on:

'Down to the war our works was supplied with machinery from Germany. When I assembled it I used to handle every detail five times over, examining it thoroughly. You couldn't deny it, intelligent hands had fashioned that machinery. I'd read books by German writers and I liked them, and I'd got into the habit of thinking of the German people with respect. True, sometimes I felt affronted that such an industrious and talented nation could stand having the filthy Hitler régime over them; but in the last resort that was their business. Then the war began in Western Europe. . . .

'And so now, as I was travelling to the front I was thinking: the Germans are strong in technique; their army, too, isn't to be sneered at. Damn it, it will be quite interesting fighting such an enemy and smashing him. We weren't made of straw in 1941 either. I must admit I didn't expect this enemy to show any special decency; what decency can you expect when you're dealing with Fascists? But I never thought I'd have to fight such a dishonest lot of ruffians as Hitler's army proved to be. Still, I'll come to that later.

'Our unit arrived at the front at the end of July. We had our first fight on the morning of the 27th. At first, with the novelty of it, it was rather frightening. Their mortars had us badly pinned down. But towards evening we got used to it a bit and gave it to them in their teeth: we drove them out of one small village. During this fight we took a group of prisoners, some fifteen men. I remember it as if it were only just now: we brought them in, they were pale and frightened. By then my men had cooled off from the fight, and every one of them gave the prisoners whatever they could: one a billy can of cabbage soup, another tobacco or cigarettes, a third treated them to tea. They slapped them on the back, called them *"Kamerad"*, and asked: "What are you fighting for, *Kameraden*?"

'But one of our men, a private, stared and stared at this affecting scene and said: "You've dribbled all over these 'friends'. They're all comrades here! But you should see what these 'comrades' are doing behind their front line, and how they deal with our wounded and with the civilian population." What he said was like a jug of cold water over us, and he turned away.

'Soon after that we went over to the offensive, and then we really did see plenty: villages burnt to the ground, hundreds of women, children and old people shot, the mutilated bodies of Red Army men who'd been taken prisoner, women raped and killed bestially, girls, and even adolescent girls. . . .

'One girl especially has remained in my memory. She was about eleven years old, evidently she was on her way to school. The Germans caught her, dragged her into a garden, raped her and killed her. She lay among crushed potato stalks, a little girl, a mere child; and her exercise-books and primers, all blood-stained, were scattered around her. Her face had been fearfully slashed with a sword; she was clutching a small, school satchel open in her hand. We covered the body with a trench cloak and stood silent. Then our men broke up, just as silently. But I remained standing there, and, I remember, I muttered like a madman: "Barkov and Polovinkin: *Physical Geography*. A Primer for sub-secondary and secondary schools." I had read this on one of the books lying in the grass, and I knew that book well: my daughter was using that same book in her fifth class.

'This was not far from Ruzhin. But in a gully close to Skvira we came upon a place of execution, where Red Army men who had been taken prisoner had been tortured. Have you ever happened to spend a little time in a butcher's shop? Well, that's more or less what this spot looked like. The branches of the trees growing in the gully were hung with blood-stained carcasses without hands, without feet, with the skin half flayed. . . . Eight dead men had been flung down in a separate heap at the bottom of the gully. It was impossible to tell what belonged to which of those tortured men: all we could see was a heap of meat cut up in large chunks; and above it, piled in a column, like trays one on top of another, were eight Red Army men's caps.

'D'you think I can put into words all I've had to see? It's impossible! No words could describe it. You have to see it for yourself. And anyway, I've said enough,' The lieutenant was silent again for a long time.

'May we smoke here?' I asked him.

'Yes. Smoke in your hand,' he answered in a voice gone hoarse.

When he had taken a draw or two he went on:

'You can understand that when we saw all the Fascists had done we went mad; nor could it be otherwise. We all realized that we had to deal not with human beings but with degenerate mongrels maddened with blood. Now we could see that with exactly the same industry as they had made machine tools and machinery, so now they were killing, raping and executing our people. . . . Later on we had to retreat again, but we fought like devils.

'Almost all the men of my company were Siberians. None the less, we defended the Ukrainian soil desperately hard. Many of my fellow countrymen died in the Ukraine, but we put down even more of the Fascists. Well, so we retreated, but we gave them quite a good lesson.'

Drawing avidly on his cigarette, he said in a rather different, gentler tone:

'There's good land in the Ukraine, and nature there is marvellous. Every village and hamlet seemed like our own native homes, perhaps because we poured out our blood there without stint; and they say blood is a bond. And when we yielded a village our hearts were griped and griped, as though under a curse. It grieved us, it grieved us till it hurt. We couldn't look one another in the face as we retreated.

'It never occurred to me then that I'd have to spend some time as a prisoner of the Fascists; but that's what happened. I had my first wound in September, but I remained in active service. But on the 21st, during a battle in the Poltava region, I was wounded again and taken prisoner.

'The German tanks broke through on our left flank, and their infantry poured after them. We fought our way out of the encirclement. That day my company suffered very great losses. Twice we beat off the enemy tank attacks; we burnt and destroyed six tanks and one armoured car, we left a hundred and twenty Nazis lying among the maize. But then they brought up mortar batteries, and we were forced to yield the height which we had held from noon till four o'clock. It had been hot all day. Not a cloud in the sky, and the sun was so hot that it really was difficult to breathe. They put down the mortar shells terribly thickly, and I remember we wanted a drink so badly that our men's lips went black with thirst, and I gave my orders in a queer, completely hoarse voice. We were running through a hollow when a mortar shell burst just in front of me. I think I saw the column of black earth and smoke, and nothing more. A shard of the shell cut through my helmet, a second caught me in the left shoulder.

'I don't remember how long I lay unconscious, but I was brought round by the sound of marching feet. I raised my head, and saw that I wasn't in the spot where I had fallen. My tunic had been taken off, and my shoulder hastily bandaged. And my helmet had gone from my head. My head also had been bandaged by someone, but the bandage had not been fastened, its end was lying on my chest. For a moment I thought my men must have dragged me away and bandaged me up as they went; and when after some difficulty I raised my head I was hoping to see them. But the men who ran up to me were not mine, they were Germans. It was the sound of their running feet that had brought me round. I could see them very distinctly, just like a good film. I groped around with my hands. I couldn't feel any weapons: no pistol, no rifle, not even grenades. One of our men had taken my map-case and arms.

' "So this is death!" I thought. What else did I think of at that moment? If you want this story to use in some future novel, then put in something of your own, for at that moment I didn't have a chance to think. The Germans were already very close, and I didn't want to die lying down. I just didn't want to, I couldn't die lying down, d'you understand? I summoned all my strength and rose on my knees, groping at the ground with my hands. By the time they came up to me I was on my feet. I stood swaying, terribly afraid I'd fall again and they'd bayonet me as I lay. They stood all around me, saying something and laughing. I said: "Well, kill me off, you swine. Kill me off now, for I'll drop in a moment." One of them struck me on the neck with his rifle butt, and I fell. But I got up again at once. They started laughing, and one of them waved his hand: "Get going, that way!" he pointed. I started walking. My face was all covered with dried blood, the blood was still running from the wound in my head, it was very warm and sticky; my shoulder hurt, and I couldn't raise my right arm. I remember I terribly wanted to lie down and not go anywhere; but all the same I went on.

'No, I had no desire whatever to die, and even less to be a prisoner. Somehow or other overcoming my dizziness and nausea, I went on – and that meant I was alive and could still function. I was tormented with thirst. My mouth was parched, and all the time my legs carried me along a sort of black blind swung in front of my eyes. I was almost unconscious, but I went on, thinking: "As soon as I've had a drink and a little rest I'll escape."

'All those who'd been taken prisoner were collected and assembled at the edge of a wood. I recognized only two Red Army men of the third company from our regiment, all the others were from an adjacent unit. The majority of the prisoners were wounded. A German lieutenant asked in bad Russian whether there were any commissars or commanders among us. Not one of us spoke. Then he said again: "Commissars and commanders step two paces forward." No one moved.

'The lieutenant walked slowly along in front of the line and picked out some sixteen men who looked as though they might be Jews. He asked each one: "Yid?", and ordered them to step out of the line without waiting for them to answer. Among those thus selected were Jews, and Armenians, and ordinary Russians with swarthy faces and black hair. They were all led a little to one side and shot down with automatics before our eyes. Then we were hurriedly searched and our papers taken, and all our personal articles. I never carried my party card in my pocket wallet, I was afraid of losing it. It was in the inner pocket of my trousers, and when they searched me they didn't find it. But you know, man is an extraordinary creature: I knew quite well that my life hung by a hair, and that if they didn't kill me when I attempted to escape they'd kill me on the road, for I'd lost so much blood that I could hardly keep up with the others. But when the search was ended and they had failed to find my party card I was so delighted that I completely forgot how thirsty I was.

'We were drawn up in marching order and driven westwards. Quite a strong escort marched on each side of us, and possibly as many as ten German motor-cyclists rode with us. They drove us along at a fast pace, and my strength began to give out. Twice I fell and got up again, and I went on, for I knew that if I lay there a moment longer and the column passed on I'd be shot on the road. That happened to a sergeant who was marching in front of me. He was wounded in the leg and could hardly walk; he groaned and sometimes cried out with the pain. We had gone barely a mile when he said aloud:

' "No, I can't go any further. Good-bye, comrades." And he sat down in the middle of the road.

'Others tried to pick him up as they passed, to set him on his feet. But he only dropped to the ground again. I remember like a dream his very pale, youthful face, his knitted brows and eyes moist with tears. The column passed on. He remained behind. I looked back and saw a motor-cyclist ride right up to him. Without getting out of his saddle, he took out his pistol, set it against the sergeant's ear and fired. By the time we reached a little river the Fascists had shot several other Red Army men who dropped out.

'And now I could see the little river, a shattered bridge and a lorry stranded beside the crossing. And there I fell face downward. Did I lose consciousness? No, I didn't. I lay stretched out full length, my mouth was filled with dust, in my fury I grated my teeth, and the sand crunched between them. But I couldn't get up. As my comrades marched past me one of them said quietly: "Get up, or they'll kill you." I started tearing with my hands at my mouth and pressing on my eyes, so as to make the pain help me to rise.

'But the column had already passed on, and I heard the wheels of a motor-cycle driving up to me. All the same, I got up! Without looking round at the motor-cyclist, swaying as though drunk, I forced myself to overtake the column and fell in with the last ranks. The German tanks and armoured cars driving through the river had made the water muddy, but we drank that warm brown wash, and it seemed sweeter than the finest spring water. I wetted my head and shoulder, and that freshened me up a lot, and my strength returned. Now I could march on with some hope that I wouldn't fall and be left lying on the road.

'We'd only just crossed the stream when we fell in with a column of medium-size German tanks coming towards us. Seeing that we were prisoners, the driver of the foremost tank accelerated and drove at full speed into our column. The leading ranks were mown down and crushed beneath its caterpillar tracks. Our escorting infantry and motor-cyclists stood watching, laughing their heads off; they bawled something to the tank men, who were looking out from their turrets, and waved their arms. Then they formed us into a column again and drove us along, while they themselves marched at the roadside. They were fond of their joke, there's no denying it.

'I made no attempt to escape that evening or that night, for I realized that I couldn't get away, I was so weak with loss of blood. And besides, we were strictly guarded, and any attempt to escape would undoubtedly have failed. But how I cursed myself later for not making the attempt! Next morning we were driven through a village in which a German force was quartered. Their infantry poured into the street to stare at us. Our escort forced us to run through the village at a trot. They thought it necessary to humiliate us in the eyes of the German troops moving up to the front. And we ran. Anyone who fell or dropped behind was shot at once. That evening we arrived at a prisoner-of-war camp.

'The yard of one of our motor-tractor service stations was surrounded with swathes of barbed wire. Inside this cage the prisoners were standing shoulder to shoulder. We were handed over to the camp guard, and they drove us with their rifle butts into the enclosure. To say that this camp was hell would be putting it mildly. There was no provision for lavatories. The men evacuated where they stood, and lay in the mud and the stinking muck. The weakest never even got up. We were given water and food once a day: a mug of water and a handful of raw millet or rotten sunflower seeds, that was all. Some days they completely forgot to give us anything.

'For two days it rained heavily. The mud in the camp was so diluted that we waded in it up to our knees. In the morning steam rose from our saturated clothing just as it rises from horses; but the rain poured down without stopping. Each night several dozen men died. We all grew weaker every day with lack of food. In addition, I was suffering tortures with my wounds.

'On the sixth day I felt that my shoulder and head wounds were hurting more than ever. They were beginning to suppurate. Then a bad smell started coming from them. On one side of the camp were the collective farm stables, and the seriously wounded Red Army men were lying in there. In the morning I asked a non-commissioned officer in charge of the guard for permission to see the doctor, who, I had been told, was seeing to the wounded. The non-com talked good Russian. He answered: "Go and see your doctor, Russian. He'll give you assistance at once."

'I didn't realize that he was being sarcastic; I was delighted, and went along to the stable.

'A third-rank army doctor met me at the entrance. He was already at the end of his tether. Thin beyond words, worn out, he was half mad with all he had had to experience. The wounded were lying on the dung litter and panting with the foul smell that filled the stable. The majority of the wounds were crawling with maggots, and those of the men who could were picking them out with their fingers and with sticks. A heap of dead prisoners was lying in there too; there hadn't been time to remove them.

' "D'you see?" the doctor asked me. "How can I help you? I haven't got a single bandage, I've got nothing. Go away; for God's sake go away. And tear off your bandages and sprinkle the wounds with ash. You'll find some fresh ash lying at the door there."

'And so I did. At the entrance the non-commissioned officer met me. He was grinning all over his face. "Well, how did you get on? Your soldiers have got a splendid doctor. Has he helped you?" I intended to pass him without speaking, but he struck me in the face with his fist, and shouted: "So you don't want to answer, you dog?" I fell down, and he kicked me again and again in the chest and on the head. He went on kicking me till he was tired. I shall never forget that Fascist as long as I live. Never! He beat me again later, more than once. Whenever he saw me through the barbed wire he ordered me to come out, and he'd start beating me, with the utmost concentration, not saying a word.

'Do you ask how I survived?

'Down to the war, before I became a mechanic, I worked as a stevedore on the Kama river; I could carry two bags of salt when helping in the unloading, with a centner in each bag. I had great strength, I didn't spare it; and altogether I've got a strong constitution. But now the main thing was that I didn't want to die, my will to resist was so strong. I'd got to return to active service to fight for our country, and I did return, in order to take vengeance on the enemy to the end.

'From that camp, which apparently was only a transit camp, I was transferred to another, some hundred kilometres away. Here the organization was exactly the same as in the transit camp: high posts wreathed with barbed wire, no roof over our heads, nothing. The food was the same, but occasionally instead of raw millet they gave us a mug of boiled rotten grain, or dragged the carcasses of dead horses into the camp, leaving it to the prisoners to share out the carrion. We ate it so as not to die of hunger – and we died in our hundreds. . . . To make things worse, in October the cold arrived; it rained without stopping, and there was frost in the mornings. We suffered cruelly from the cold. I managed to strip a dead Red Army man of his tunic and greatcoat. But even these didn't protect me from the cold. However, by now we'd got used to hunger.

'We were guarded by soldiers who had grown fat on plunder. So far as their characters were concerned they were all carved from one block. They were nothing but absolute ruffians. For instance, this was their idea of amusing themselves. In the morning a lance-corporal would come up to the wire and say through an interpreter:

' "There's to be a food distribution in a moment. The distribution will take place on the left."

'The lance-corporal goes away. Everybody capable of standing hurries over to the left side of the camp. We wait an hour, two, three. Hundreds of trembling, living skeletons standing in the piercing wind. Just standing and waiting.

'And suddenly at the other side of the camp guards come hurrying up. They throw chunks of horseflesh over the wire. Driven by hunger, the whole crowd of prisoners rush to that side, and a struggle begins over the pieces of flesh smarmed with mud.

'The guards stand laughing their heads off, and suddenly there's a long burst from a machine-gun. Cries and groans. The prisoners rush back to the left side, leaving the dead and wounded lying. A tall first lieutenant, he was the camp commandant, comes up to the wire, accompanied by an interpreter. Hardly able to suppress his laughter, he says:

' "Disgusting disorders have taken place during the food distribution. If they're repeated I shall give orders for you Russian swines to be shot down ruthlessly. Take away your dead and wounded." The Nazi soldiers crowding behind the commandant are nearly dying with laughter. The commandant's "clever" trick is very much to their liking.

We would silently drag the dead out of the camp and bury them not far away, in a gully. . . . In that camp we were beaten with fists, with sticks, with butt ends. They beat us up at any moment, out of boredom or for amusement. My wounds started to heal; but then, I suppose through the constant dampness and the beatings, they opened again and hurt unbearably. But I was still alive, and I hadn't lost hope of escaping. . . . We slept just as we were, in the mud; there was no straw litter, nothing. We lay huddled together in a solid mass. All night there was a continual shifting about among us; those lying in the mud at the bottom grew cold, and those at the top felt the cold too.

'The days passed like an oppressive dream. With every day I grew weaker and weaker. Now even a child could have knocked me down. At times I looked in horror at my shrivelled hands, with only skin drawn over them, and thought: "How shall I ever get away from here?" And it was then that I cursed myself for not attempting to escape during those first few days. After all, if I'd been killed then I shouldn't have had all this terrible suffering to bear.

'Winter arrived. We dug away the snow and slept on the frozen ground. Our numbers grew fewer and fewer. . . . At last it was announced that in a few days we were to be sent to work. We all came to life. In every one of us was born the hope – though very feeble at least it was hope – that possibly we would succeed in escaping.

'That night was still, but frosty. Just before dawn we heard gunfire. Everybody around me began to stir . And when the roar was repeated suddenly someone said aloud:

' "Comrades, our men are attacking."

'And then occurred something unimaginable: the entire camp scrambled to their feet, as though by command. Even men who hadn't got up for several days managed to rise. All around us we heard burning whispering and suppressed sobbing. Someone next to me burst into tears and cried like a woman. I too . . . I too . . .' Lieutenant Gerasimov said hurriedly, in a broken voice. But then, recovering his control, he continued more calmly: 'The tears rolled down my cheeks too, freezing in the wind. . . . Someone began feebly to sing the "International", and we all took it up with thin, grating voices. The guards opened fire on us with machine-guns and automatics, they shouted an order: "Lie down!" I lay down, pressing my body into the snow, and wept like a child. But they were tears not only of joy but of pride in our people. The Fascists could kill us, disarmed and disabled as we were with hunger; they could torture us; but they couldn't break our spirit, and they never will! They'd chosen the wrong people to attack, I tell you straight.'

I didn't manage to hear the finish of Lieutenant Gerasimov's story that night: he was urgently summoned to the regimental staff. But a few days later we met again. His dug-out smelt of mould and pine resin. The lieutenant was sitting on a bench, huddled, with his large hands, fingers interlocked, resting on his knees. Looking at him, I couldn't help thinking it must have been in the prisoner-of-war camp that he had grown used to sitting thus, with fingers interlocked, silent for hours and oppressively, fruitlessly thinking.

'You ask how I managed to escape? I'll tell you. Soon after the night we'd heard the gunfire we were sent to work on the construction of fortifications. The frosts were replaced by a thaw. Rain started falling. We were driven out to the north of the camp. Once more it was the same all over again: men who were exhausted fell, were shot and were left lying on the road.

'And I must mention that one man was shot by a non-commissioned officer simply for picking up a frozen potato from the road. We were marching across a potato field. A sergeant, a Ukrainian named Gonchar, picked up that accursed potato and tried to hide it. The non-commissioned officer noticed him. Without saying a word, he went up to Gonchar and shot him in the neck. The column was halted and drawn up. "All this is the property of the German state," said the non-commissioned officer, sweeping his arm around. "Any of you who arbitrarily takes anything will be shot."

'In one village we passed through the women started throwing us pieces of bread and baked potatoes. Some of our men managed to pick them up, but most of us failed. The escort opened fire at the windows, and we were ordered to march faster. But the children – they're always without fear – ran on some distance ahead and put bread down right on the road. And we picked it up. I managed to get hold of a large boiled potato. I shared it half and half with my neighbour, and we ate it, skin and all. I've never eaten a more tasty potato!

'The fortifications were being constructed in a forest. The Germans reinforced our guards considerably, and gave us spades. I didn't feel like building fortifications, I felt far more like destroying them!

'That very same day, late in the afternoon, I made up my mind. I crawled out of the hole we were digging, took the spade in my left hand and went up to the guard. I'd already observed that the other Germans were in a trench, and that apart from the one in charge of our group none of the guards was near.

' "My spade's broken; look!" I muttered as I approached the soldier. For a brief moment the thought flashed through my mind that if I didn't have the strength to lay him flat at the first blow I was done for. Evidently the guard noticed something in the expression on my face. He shrugged his shoulders to slip off the sling of his automatic, and at that moment I struck him with the spade right in the face. I couldn't hit him on the head: he was wearing a helmet. But I did have sufficient strength to send him headlong without his making a sound.

'Now I had an automatic and three cartridges in my hands. I started running. But now it seemed I couldn't run! I hadn't the strength, and that was the end of it! I halted, took breath and again set off at barely a trot. The other side of a gully the forest was thicker, and I made my way there. I don't remember how many times I fell, got up and fell again. But with every minute I was getting farther away. Sobbing and panting with weariness, I had made my way through the thicket to the other side of a hill when far behind me I heard automatics rattling, and then a cry. But now it wouldn't be so easy to catch me.

'Twilight began to fall. But if the Germans did manage to get on my trail and come up close I'd keep just one last cartridge for myself! That thought gave me fresh courage; I went on more quietly and cautiously.

'I spent the night in the forest. I saw a village not half a mile away, but I was afraid of going there in case I ran into Germans.

'Next day I was picked up by partisans. I lay resting in their dug-out for a couple of weeks, recovering my strength. At first they were rather suspicious of me, even though I took out my party card, which I had sewn into the lining of my greatcoat in the camp, and showed it to them. But later on, when I took part in their operations, their attitude changed at once. And it was there I opened the account of the Fascists I've killed. I keep the account faithfully to this day, and the figure is gradually approaching a hundred.

'In January the partisans conducted me through the front lines. I spent about a month in hospital. They removed the piece of mortar shell from my shoulder, and the rheumatism and all the other ailments I acquired in the camp I shall cure after the war. I spent a week at home; but I couldn't stay there any longer. I was longing for the front, and that's all I can say. Others can say what they like, but my place is here to the end.'

We said good-bye to each other at the entrance to the dug-out. Gazing thoughtfully at the glade, which was flooded with bright sunlight, the lieutenant said:

'And we've learnt how to make war properly, and how to hate, and how to love. On such a whetstone as war all one's feelings get sharpened splendidly. You might think that love and hatred simply cannot be put side by side; you know the old saying: "You can't harness a horse and a nervous doe in the one cart." But in our case they are harnessed together, and they draw the cart splendidly! I have a bitter hatred for the Fascists, because of all they've done to my country and to me personally; and at the same time with all my heart I love my people and I don't want them to have to suffer under the Fascist yoke. And it's that which compels me, and all of us, to fight with such fury: just those two feelings, incarnate in action, will bring us victory. And if love for our country is preserved in our hearts and continues to be preserved as long as those hearts beat we shall always carry our hatred at the ends of our bayonets. Forgive me if this all sounds rather complicated, but that's what I think,' Lieutenant Gerasimov ended. And for the first time since I had known him he smiled simply and pleasantly, a boyish smile.

And now for the first time too I noticed that this thirty-two-year-old lieutenant, broken by the deprivations he had suffered, yet still strong and as tough as an oak, had dazzling white hair at his temples. And that whiteness gained at the cost of great suffering was so pure that the white thread of a spider-web clinging to his cap was lost to sight as it touched his temple, and I could not discern it, no matter how hard I tried.

1942

A Letter to American Friends

It will soon be two years that we have been waging war, a war harsh and oppressive. You know that we have succeeded in halting and throwing back the enemy. Possibly you are not fully aware of all the difficulties this war imposes on every one of us. And I would like our friends to know about them.

As a war correspondent I have been on the Southern, the South-Western and the Western fronts. At this moment I am writing a novel, entitled *They fought for their Country*. In it I want to reveal the burden of the people's struggle for their freedom. But now, before the novel is finished, I want to write to you not in my capacity as a writer, but simply as a citizen of a country allied to yours.

The war has entered into the destiny of every one of us with all the force resulting from the attempt of one nation completely to annihilate, to devour another. The events at the front, the events of total war have left their ineradicable traces in the life of every one of us. I have lost my seventy-year-old mother, who was killed by a bomb dropped from a German plane when the Germans bombed a district centre which had no strategic importance whatever, when they were putting into effect their brigand-like calculations: all they wanted was to force out the inhabitants, so that the people could not drive their cattle into the steppe to hide them from the approaching German Army. My house, my library, were destroyed by German mortars. I have already lost many friends at the front, both of my profession and other fellow countrymen. For a long time I was separated from my family. During this time my son was seriously ill, and I had no means of helping my family. But after all, in the final account these are personal misfortunes, the personal sorrows of each one of us. But their burdens make up the magnitude of the general national disaster which people suffer when war enters into their lives. Our personal sorrows

205

must not hide from us the sufferings of our nation, sufferings which no writer or artist has yet succeeded in telling to the world.

For it must be remembered that vast expanses of our land, hundreds of thousands of our people's lives, have been seized by the enemy, the most brutal of any known to history. The legends of antiquity tell us of the blood-letting invasions of the Huns, the Mongols and other savage tribes. All that fades in the light of what the German Fascists are doing in their war against us. With my own eyes I have seen large villages burnt to the ground, and the hamlets of my fellow-countrymen – who were the heroes of my books – I have seen orphans, I have seen people robbed of blood and happiness, horribly mutilated bodies, thousands of mutilated lives. All this has been brought to our country at the order of their leader, who is obsessed by a mania for blood.

That same fate is being prepared by Nazism for all the countries in the world; and for your country too, for your home, and your life.

We want you to take a sober look ahead. We greatly value your friendly, disinterested aid. We know and value the extent of your efforts, the difficulties which are associated with the production and especially the supply of materials to our country. I myself have seen your lorries in the Don steppes, your splendid aeroplanes in battles with those who bombed our villages. There is not one man among us who has not been conscious of your friendly support.

But I want to speak to you very frankly, as we have been taught to speak by the war. Our country, our nation has suffered many wounds from the war. Only now is the struggle beginning to burn fiercely. And we want to see our friends side by side with us in the battle. We summon you to the battle. We offer you not simply the friendship of our nations, but the friendship of soldiers.

If territorial reasons do not allow us to fight in the literal sense side by side, we want to know that the powerful blows of your armies are being directed against the rear of the enemy who has invaded our country.

We know the enormous effects of your air bombardment

of our common enemy's industrial centres. But war is war only when all forces are engaged in it. The enemy confronting us is perfidious, powerful and he hates our nation and yours to death. It is impossible to come through this war with unsullied hands. It demands sweat and blood. Otherwise it will only take a triple toll of them. The consequences of vacillation can be irreparable. You have not yet seen the blood of your dear ones on the threshold of your homes. I have, and so I have the right to speak to you so frankly.

1943

A Word on our Country

Winter . . . night.

Remain a little while in the silence and solitude, dear compatriot and friend; close your eyes, recall the recent past and with the eyes of your mind you will see.

. . . A cold, whitish mist is spectrally wreathing over the forests and marshes of Belorussia, over the empty, long-deserted dug-outs overgrown with faded bracken, over the collapsing trenches and the snipers' nests flooded with rusty water. Faintly at their bottom glimmer rifle cartridge cases going green with time.

Before the mighty northern wind the pines of Smolensk and Sub-Moscow, scarred and racked by shells, bow their crowns and rustle mutely.

The fine, white, fluffy snow falls plentifully, as though hastening to cover the earth tousled by war in the environs of Lenin's immortal city, the land sacred to our people.

Sunny shadows slip over the resurrected fields of the Ukraine, which were ploughed, reploughed again and again by shells and still recall the thunderous roar of unprecedented battles.

Around Kursk and Oriel, around Voroniezh and Tula, over the age-old Russian earth which groaned for three years under the weight of tens of thousands of tanks, a streaming blizzard strews its snow; shrivelled by the frost, the last leaves fall from the trees; and everywhere – in the fields, on the highways and the country byways, up and down the land trodden over step by step by the patient feet of our infantry – the finest in the world – they gleam redly like blood spurting up through the snow.

In the boundless steppes around Stalingrad, where every clod of earth is sown with shards of once death-dealing metal as though with grain, where the picked Nazi divisions were turned to dust and ashes, the bitter wind from the other side of the Volga chases the gypsophila; it is as gloomy and rusted brown as the hulls of the German tanks and motorized guns, scattered everywhere about the steppe and now silenced for ever.

But in the Crimea, and in the azure foothills of the Caucasus, the dazzling white threads of gossamer still float in the chilly transparent air. In the pleasant morning dawns, where at one time the sounds of battle never ceased, the trenches and craters, feathered round their edges with shaggy scrub, are now laced with gossamer as with a silvery net, and every tiny thread sags and quivers gently, all embroidered with the tiny, glittering tears of dew. . . .

But from Stalingrad to Berlin and from the Caucasus to the Barents Sea, wherever, my friend, your gaze may come to rest, everywhere you will see the graves of soldiers fallen in battle, graves dear to the heart of our Mother Country. And in that moment you will recall more keenly those innumerable sacrifices which your country suffered in defence of our native Soviet régime, and the words will resound in your memory like a majestic requiem: 'Eternal glory to the heroes who fell in the struggle for the freedom and independence of our Mother Country.'

Recalling the past, you will involuntarily think – you cannot but think of how many orphaned people were left in your Mother Country after the war. In this winter night, long and ample for bitter memories, many a widow who lost her husband in the war and is now left alone will press her palms to her ageing face; and in the nocturnal darkness the burning tears, as bitter as wormwood, will scorch her fingers. And before he falls to sleep many a child, wounded for a lifetime by the death of him who, faithful to military duty and oath, perished in the struggle for the socialist Mother Country, will feel his heart torn with unchildlike yearnings at a chance recollection. But perhaps it will be thus: in a small room, where a mournful silence has reigned for years already, an old man will go across to his grey-haired wife and partner, who without a word is weeping over her fallen sons; he will glance into the faded eyes, from which that most bitter suffering in all the world, the suffering of a mother, has squeezed out all tears, and will say in a husky, trembling voice: 'Now, no more, mother. Don't go on so, I ask you. We're not the only ones with such sorrow.' And without waiting for an answer, he will turn away to the window, will clear his throat and swallow dry, aged tears as brief as sobs. And then, standing long silent, he will gaze at the misted glass with unseeing eyes.

My dear friend and fellow countryman: may our hatred for the enemy, even though he is vanquished, never grow cold. And may it boil and seethe in our hearts with tenfold fury at those for whom there is no name in any human language; those who still are not satiated with profits squeezed out of the blood of millions, who in their blind, satanic madness are preparing a new war for suffering humanity.

Their sinister names will be pronounced with curses and loathing by every honest man in the world; they are destined by history to perish sombrely, and time is already industriously weaving strong nooses for them. But so long as they are alive, so long as, without stint, they spend millions on the creation of atom bombs, on the preparation of a new, monstrous war, may our ineradicable hatred for them live on. It will come in useful at the requisite moment.

Remember, friend: for all the thirty years the Soviet régime has existed the Land of the Soviets has not known defeats either in wars or in the overcoming of any difficulties; at the price of incredible sacrifices and national sufferings we have emerged the victors even in this last and greatest of wars. But the sacrifices borne for the sake of the salvation of the Mother Country have not reduced our powers, and the bitterness of the unforgettable losses has not lowered our spirit.

It sometimes happens that in the midst of the wheat fields, among the flowering mass of various grasses the steppe wormwood spreads and bushes in an azure mist, and so the grain, as it fills and ripens, gathers into itself the bitterness of the wormwood. For fine eating, for the pastry-cook's products, flour from such grain is no good. But grain does not cease to be grain because it has a bitter taste. And to him who is working, washing himself with salty sweat, it seems pleasant; and it gives man the same abundant strength, so that on the morrow he will have something to expend in his heavy, exhausting labour.

The people – the creator – is healing the wounds inflicted by the war with astonishing, with fabulous swiftness: the devastated cities and incinerated villages are rising from the ruins, the mines of our native Don Basin have been restored to life, the stalks of the grain are already showing golden over those fields where two years ago thistles and scrub grew in a wild brush, an evil, impenetrable waste; the chimneys of the reconstructed works and factories are smoking, new industrial enterprises are being born where recently were only backwoods and wildernesses. And even the Soviet man, who has seen many things, and has long believed in the creative strength of his toiling genius, when he learns of the pre-scheduled start-up of a restored metallurgical giant or of the All-Union record of a Stakhanovite hitherto unknown to our country, flings out his hands in joyous astonishment.

But the pride of the Mother Country, the working class of Leningrad, is already calling on the workers to fulfil the Five Year Plan in four years. And already the majestic contours of a new, splendid life are visibly arising before one's eyes. . . .

Truly, unprecedentedly powerful is the Party which has been able to organize, train, equip and lead the nation behind it to the accomplishing of exploits previously unknown to history. Truly, great and invincible is the nation which has not only succeeded in maintaining its independence and shattering all its enemies but has become the light of hope for the workers of all the world.

To be a faithful son of such a people and such a Party – is that not, my friend, the very greatest happiness in life for us and our contemporaries! And are not we who are alive today inspired to incessant labour and new exploits by our harsh responsibility for the fate of the Mother Country, for the work of the Party, a responsibility which we bear not only towards the coming generations but towards the glorious memory of those who fought and went to their death in defence of the Mother Country.

In these memorable Lenin days the workers of the world bow their heads just as they did twenty-four years ago, just as they always do on the day of this mournful anniversary, remembering him who showed humanity the road to a new life.

In 1919 he – the leader of a great party and the creator of the first socialist state in the world – spoke unforgettable words:

'For the first time in the world the authority of the State is constructed here in Russia in such a way that only the workers, only the toiling peasants, excluding exploiters, constitute mass organizations – the Soviets, and to these Soviets is transferred all the state power. That is why, no matter how much the representatives of the bourgeoisie in all countries slander Russia, everywhere in the world the word "Soviet" has not only become comprehensible, it has become popular, it has become beloved of the workers, of all the toilers.'

'The Soviet government,' said Lenin, 'is the road to Socialism found by the masses of workers, and therefore – certain; and therefore – invincible.'

Our country, the country of invincible Socialism, stands unconquerable in the world.

Friends know from what inexhaustible sources we have drawn and still draw our strength both for war and for peaceable labour.

The enemies remain enemies: some simply slander, slander with all their intrinsic impudence, primitively and coarsely; others hurriedly take out from the dusty archives their thoroughly moth-eaten meditations on the 'enigma of the Slavonic soul', on 'Russian fanaticism' and, shamefacedly covering their poverty and meanness with these thread-bare clothes, pretend that they cannot understand at all whence the Soviet people derive their indomitable strength.

But at the price of long years of suffering and great revolutionary struggle the people have found for themselves the only just régime; with full resolution and valour they have confirmed it with their blood, their labour; and no powers whatever can shake their faith in that régime.

How thorough has been the spiritual transformation of the Russian man, and more especially the peasant, during the existence of the Soviet system, and what new and miraculous qualities he has acquired during the years of the Five Year Plans, when he was a collective farmer, you will see more distinctly when you compare the recent past with the present day.

In January 1930, at a time when total ~~collectivization~~ was being carried out in the Don region, I had to travel from the station of Millerovo to Vioshenska. Neither my driver nor I had any hope that we would cover the 168 kilometres of road quickly. The horses were tired, the road, judging by reports, was intolerable – nothing but pot-holes and ruts for almost the whole way – a low ground wind was blowing across the steppe, and the heavy lilac clouds which rose in a sombre pile in the east presaged imminent bad weather.

We set out at dawn. Outside the town the bitter scent of coal slag and the smoke of lighted stoves was replaced by the sweet clean smell of fresh snow, and the pungent tang of horses' sweat. The deep winter silence was broken only by the squeak of the sledge runners, the snorts of the horses and, occasionally, as we dropped into a deep rut, the knock of a swingle-tree against the sledge centre-pole.

My driver, a bearded, elderly Cossack, who nevertheless still had a youthful stateliness, with impudent, deep-set little eyes and dashingly combed forelock, proved to be unusually garrulous. At first he drove without speaking, whistling morosely, thinking his own thoughts; I could see only his broad back, the tight-fitting short sheepskin, the brown, furrowed neck and the rimed forelock breaking loose from under his dashingly cocked cap, which had ear-flaps and a neck-flap. But I had only to ask him some question for him to turn round at once, thrust the reins under his seat and say with a smile:

'Brother, you should see what's going on in our villages. . . . You never saw the likes of it!'

'Why, what's going on?'

'Well, the collective farms have started up, and now the people are sitting on and on in meetings, as I doubt whether they know how to, even in Moscow.'

'What d'you mean?'

'Why, they sit for three days on end, day and night.'

'And have many of the people in your village joined the collective farm?'

'They've been split in two halves: some have joined, but the rest are still hesitating, like sheep before the gate into the

213

yard. So they sit all together and even come to blows, like young cockerels. It's both funny and serious; there's no controlling it! I've got a neighbour, Mikhey Fomich. He's a very old man, a real ancient, but he goes outside only for his old man's needs and spends all night in the village Soviet, and he has his food there too. His old woman brings him cabbage soup in a pot, and while she's wading through the snow the soup gets quite cold. Fomich sips at the cold soup and then sits still again, like a nail in the wall. . . . It's amazing what an activist he's turned out to be!'

'Is he a collective farmer?'

'A fine collective farmer he is! He's an activist in the opposite direction, one of the quite comfortable middle peasants. He doesn't speak right out against the collective farm, he just sits very quietly in the back row and drips poison, sometimes from the holy scriptures, and sometimes thinking it up for himself. I went along to the meeting, too, before I came on this trip. We sit there packed tight, I at the end, this same Mikhey Fomich on my left and next to him the widow Yefrosina Melnikova. And Fomich nags and nags away, and won't let anyone listen. And so she says to him: "Don't interrupt." Then she says it again, but he doesn't give way. A party man from the district is talking about the collective farm but Fomich goes on whispering his remarks – "and that, of course, won't be good", and something else "will be quite bad". . . . Then he jostles Yefrosina with his elbow and says very quietly: "First they'll make you socialize the cattle, my good woman, and then they'll be driving us all to sleep under the same blanket. A man I trust told me so." But she answers jokingly: "What of it? I'm a widow, I shan't lose by it. Only God grant that I don't have to sleep beside you, for then I shall certainly drop out of the collective farm." Well, Fomich smelt a rat and asked rather louder: "What made you say that, you filthy woman?" Froska got angry at that remark, and said quite loud: "Because, you old devil, you stink of mouse's turds a mile off, like an empty granary." So they start arguing, and then the fun began. He says to her: "You're quite shameless, you so-and-so, and you've forgotten God." But she says to him: "It's all right for you, you semi-kulak, to speak against the collective farm; you've got two yoke of oxen, and a pair of horses. But have I got to spend all my life in need with my one little cow?" He swears at her good and strong, but she swears back with a woman's twisted curses, and the affair came to blows. Just as if it were the old days, Fomich pulled off her kerchief and seized her by the hair. Yefrosina, she's no fool, caught hold of his little beard. She's a young woman, and strong, and she seized a handful of hair and it all came away in her hand. They had to separate them by force, as true as I'm here. Afterwards I took a look at Fomich, and he had only half a beard, it was just as if a cow had licked the other half away with its tongue. I couldn't help laughing: but I checked myself and said to him: "Don't you come along to these meetings, Mikhey Fomich, or the women will pluck you like a dead cock, and won't even leave a bit of fluff for breeding." But he gives me a haughty look and says: "I'll lose my last hair before I leave the meeting." He's turned out to be a terrible activist, you'd never have thought he had it in him.'

'But have you joined the collective farm, Prokofievich?' I asked interestedly.

Prokofievich measuredly stroked his chestnut beard with its gingery flush, and screwed up his restless little blue eyes mischievously:

'I'm in no hurry. . . .'

'Why not?'

'You see, it's like this: when I'm invited to a wedding or a party I never sit down before the others. If you wait till all the others have sat down and you sit at the end, if you need to you can slip away from the table quicker.' So that I should not be left in any doubt as to his meaning, he added: 'But maybe I don't like what's on the table, and so what the devil have I got to sit right in the middle for, under the ikon?'

I told him with a laugh that if he waited and thought about it too long he might not get any seat at the table. But he shook his head obstinately:

'I keep a sharp look-out around me. They're inviting me to join the collective farm too; according to my means I'm nothing but a wavering middle peasant: all I possess are a pair of horses and a stupid little cow. But if I'm a waverer, as they call me at the meetings, I want to have a real good look at this collective farm. But to fling myself into it head first, that's all rather . . . not quite . . . not a lot to . . .'

'So you're just a little afraid?'

'No; I'm not the sort to be afraid, but I am a bit cautious. Just in case. You tell me, rather: what sort of life has one got to be more afraid of, the collective farmer's or the individual farmer's? I'm only afraid of making a mistake, because I've learned my lesson from my youth up, and I know: sometimes you expect trouble from one direction, but it comes at you from another: and a very good health to you! For instance, I'll tell you a certain story. Thirty years ago my late parents engaged me to a bride, not in our own village, but in another. We drove over to take a look at her. And I was a heroic sort of lad, but when I took my first look at her my heart sank, and I felt it was sticking somewhere in my gullet. . . . I saw standing in front of me a real fighter of a girl, daring, sparkling eyes and of an impossible beauty, like a sky-blue flower! So she looked at me, and I couldn't say a word, I was as silent as a corpse. Well, they left us together in the room. We sit side by side on the chest, but I still remained speechless, looking her over and blinking. One thing struck me at once: her hands were much too small, just like a child's. I remember I thought even then: with hands like those she couldn't lift a sacred garland, so what sort of worker would she prove on the farm? That's what I was thinking, but my tongue refused to wag. We sat a long time saying nothing. She sat patiently, patiently; but at last she leaned across to me and asked in a whisper: "So you're dumb, it seems?" I only shook my head, but I still didn't say a word, they just wouldn't come: I could have wept! Then she knitted her brows and said sternly: "Well, then, show me your tongue! Perhaps you've bitten it through on the road through being shaken about?" I acted like a fool and put out my tongue. . . . Oh, hell, I feel the shame of it to this very day when I remember what a fool I showed myself. And then she laughed and laughed till the tears came into her eyes. She laughed with her hands pressed to her chest, she couldn't get her breath for laughing. At last she called: "Mummy, come here! Look at him! Why, he's a perfect fool! How can I ever marry him?" So you see, brother, what an unpleasant turn the matter had taken for me.

'And I felt mad with her, though I myself felt like laughing. But then I happened to notice her teeth and I was struck dumb again. Her teeth were so white, a dazzling white, as white as foam, and one was set close to another and they were sharp, and she had a mouth full of them, like a yearling wolf. "Well, that shows me," I thought; "I'm caught. With teeth like those she could easily tear a young heifer to pieces, and what will happen to me if I marry her? If we happen to have some family disagreement, she won't master me with her hands, they're rather small for a fight. But God grant she doesn't bring her teeth into action, for then my skin will fly off me in bits and pieces. She could quite easily tear enough skin off me to make a pair of reins."

'And whether out of fear or out of anger, my tongue started wagging, and I said: "You look out, my girl; you're laughing today, but if you marry me you might have to weep." But she says in answer: " 'The blind man said: we'll see.' We don't know as yet who'll make who weep."

'And so we came together. And do you think she got the mastery of me with her teeth? No, that's not how it happened!

'She didn't make her teeth blunt on me, the Lord didn't allow it. Even now, though she's an old woman, even now she's got a full head of teeth, and she cracks cherry stones, the devil, as if she was husking sunflower seeds. It was with her little hands she seized the power! Year by year, little by little, she got the upper hand of me. But now, maybe, I'd try to resist, but it's too late; I've grown used to the collar, I've grown patient in my misfortunes, like a lousy little horse to the mange. I'm peaceable enough even when I'm drunk, and when sober I'm still meeker. And so she, the enemy, lords it over me as she likes.

'Sometimes of a holiday we older Cossacks clubbed together to drink a litre each, for the sake of old memories: who did his service where, who fought against who, and we'd sing songs. . . . Well, no matter how much a foal kicks up its heels in the meadow, the time comes for it to run to its mother. I'd arrive home a little tipsy like, and find my wife standing at the door

217

with a frying pan ready like a gun in her hand. It would be a long story to tell you all of it, and it's uninteresting anyway. . . . I'll say just one thing: she taught me to open the door with my back, I don't mind telling you. No matter how drunk I got, as soon as I reached the porch I'd give myself the command: "Stop, Ignat Prokofievich! Left about turn!" I'd turn right round and go into my hut backwards. That way was more reliable; I got hurt less. . . . In the morning I'd wake up, my back aching as though someone had threshed peas on it. Beside me stands a plate of cabbage water, but my wife would be missing. In my drunken fit I might have turned my temper loose on her, but even the devil with a lantern wouldn't have found her till the evening. And of course by the evening my heart had burnt itself out. . . . And then she turns up and looks at me so sweetly: "Hello, Ignat Prokofievich, how are you getting on?" "I'm alive, praise be!" I tell her, "but it's a pity you didn't fall into my hands this morning, damn you! I'd have chopped you up into sticks to heat the stove with!"

'She's continually asking me to make a new oak handle for the frying pan, but I'm not all that slow-witted! I'll choose for that handle a piece of wood that's half rotten, and I'll shave it very thin, just so that she can lift the frying pan without it breaking. And that's how we live, little by little. . . .

'What was the point of my telling you all this? I know: just to say that when I got married I was afraid of my wife's teeth, but I have to suffer from her hands. And it's the same now: you're afraid of the collective farm, but look out lest you have to live like a wolf as an individual farmer. . . . And if you do remain an individual farmer keep a still tongue in your head. Don't you agree?'

Smiling into his beard, Prokofievich winked and screwed up his eyes, as though saying, for all his mischievous look: I'm not so simple and inoffensive as you might think. But you can take all I've said as you wish; as a joke if you like, or serious if you don't.

He was silent for a few minutes, but then in a sad tone that had no hint of merriment in it, he said:

'The devil knows what to do! Well, we'll see if we live as long.'

Suddenly rising on his seat, he laid the knout about his horses with unexpected harshness, and shouted:

'You've been listening to other people's conversation, you devilish individuals! I'll twist your tails for you!'

The snow, which had been sprinkling down thinly, soon began falling in large flakes; the wind blew more fiercely, slanting drifts lay across the road, and the tired horses, which had been moving at a heavy jog-trot, again dropped to a walking pace, their flanks shaggy with rime.

We arrived at the village of Lower Yablonovka in the dead of night. Only in one of the little huts of this large village was a light faintly shining through the frosted, unshuttered window.

We asked to be allowed to spend the night there. While Prokofievich was unharnessing the horses, I went into the hut. By the bed, which was piled high with all sorts of junk, an old man was sitting hunched gloomily, his legs wide apart, on a low, lopsided stool. A small black lamb was asleep at his feet, rolled up in a ball on some straw litter. Its curly wool gleamed dully, lit by the vague light of a paraffin lamp. The master seemed to answer our greeting reluctantly; he took one brief glance at me and again drooped his head. One large, coarse hand, hanging below his knee, was gently and tenderly stroking the lamb; his thick fingers graciously fingered the gleaming black little curls, only lightly touching them.

An old woman lying on the stove said:

'Why don't you go and show the man where to put up the horses?'

The master silently flung on a coat and went out.

'You seem very late in getting to bed; is there something wrong on the farm?' I asked.

Obviously delighted to have a chance of talking to a passing stranger, the old woman readily answered:

'Ah, my dear, what sort of farm have we got now? It looks as though we've farmed away all we had. . . . Only the wind goes playing about our empty yards, lording it as it wishes. All we have left is two sheep and this little lamb. We had a dog, but even he has run off somewhere from our empty yard, there was nothing left for him to guard.'

With a grunt the old woman got up, let her feet in their

woollen stockings hang down from the stove, and, short-sightedly screwing up her eyes at the little yellow flame of the lamp, went on:

'But my old man, by the true God, has got a little touched in the head. This is the fourth night he hasn't slept a wink. He lies down each evening, but then he lights the lamp, sits down by the table, rolls himself a cigarette and sits and sits, smoking, saying nothing. . . . These last few days I've grown quite unused to the sound of his voice. Believe me, by the morning the room's so full of smoke I'm almost choking and my head's spinning. But you can't say a word to him: he just gives me an animal look, slams the door and goes out into the yard without speaking.'

With the movement common from time immemorial to all simple women, she rested her cheek on her hand, and drooped her head mournfully:

'And for four days now he's hardly eaten a thing. He sits down at the table, holds the spoon in his hand and lays it down again, then he reaches for his tobacco pouch and rolls himself a cigarette. And why that tobacco doesn't make him go mad I just can't imagine. He's gone quite dark in the face, he never eats a thing, he only smokes and smokes. He's quite a healthy man really, his sickness is mental, and it gnaws at him. . . .'

'What sort of sickness d'you think it is?' I asked, though I already had a good idea of the cause of the old man's trouble.

'It's quite clear what it is: we joined the collective farm last week. My master led away the horse and he himself drove a pair of oxen and a cow to the communal yard; and at the moment we've only got the sheep. And in a yard without animals you might as well be in a graveyard.'

Leaning over towards me, she whispered confidentially:

'Yesterday he chopped down an apple tree in the orchard for firewood. A living tree! I couldn't help groaning: my old man had lost his senses. And the tree bore such lovely early apples, it was a joy. But now it's just as if he has no pity for anything, he has no need of anything, for everything has become the property of other people, as you might say. Nobody forced him to join the collective farm, he put his name down of his own free will. But now look what's happened to the man! Before he was so cheerful, he came back from the meeting and said: "Well, old woman, we're collective farmers now. I put my name down today. We'll be working in co-operative gangs. Maybe we shan't live so well in the collective farm, but, on the other hand, we'll be carrying a lighter burden on our backs; now we're old it's time we had a rest." I wept aloud, but he laughed: "You fool, it'll be an easier life for us old people, so wipe your eyes." But after he'd taken the animals from the yard it was as though someone had exchanged him for another man. . . . He's tried to get the cow back; but who knows whether they'll let us have it? . . .'

We heard the sound of crunching snow outside, and men's voices. The old woman said no more, and nimbly covered herself right over her head with a ragged old blanket.

His frozen felt boots thumping hollowly, Prokofievich came into the room with the master following him.

Over supper my driver tried again and again to draw the old man into conversation, but without success: he either kept silent or answered curtly, in monosyllables, and was obviously oppressed by his garrulous visitor. At last Prokofievich took offence, spread his sheepskin coat on the bench and lay down to sleep. The old woman also doubtless dropped off; only the old man remained active; he brought in an armful of firewood chopped small, lit a small stove set up by the bed and sat down by the fire. Feeling the warmth, the lamb also shifted closer to the stove. It stood swaying for some time on its feeble, crooked legs, then quietly started to bleat, calling for its mother. Then it lay down again at the old man's feet, fixing its demonic, swollen yellow eyes on the fire. The rainbow reflections of the flames flickered in its slanting eyeballs.

'There's an insect for you! It's only been alive a few days, but it understands already where it's better off: it makes for the fire.' The old man nodded at the lamb and smiled almost imperceptibly.

The long silence was broken, and I resolved to ask:
'Why don't you get to bed, master?'
'I don't feel sleepy, so what's the point?'
Evidently his unexpressed sorrow brimmed over, he found

it impossible to keep silent any longer, and he began to talk, occasionally giving me a glance from his sunken, moody eyes:

'Sleep never has been sweet for old people, but these days it's quite impossible. You see, one of the people working in the government starts thinking a little about our life as grain-growers, but what he thinks is to no point. Recently a pleni-potentiary from the district visited our village. I was driving all my cattle to hand over to the collective farm, and he says: "Now you'll take life easily, old fellow, and have a rest. You won't have any cares now. You won't have to worry about food for the cattle, you won't have to go out and bring them in. You'll have a winter life all the year round: eat, drink and sleep on the stove. Perhaps in the spring you'll do what you can to help the collective farm, or you'll give a hand with the harvest."

'A light man thinks lightly. Did I really join the collective farm in order to be a parasite? Of course I need to work so long as I can stand on my two feet, so long as I've got strength in my hands. Otherwise, without something to do, in my boredom I'll be giving up the ghost. But the way he talked it works out that I've handed my cattle over to someone else and now I ought to cross myself: thank God I'm free of my burdens. But it doesn't work out at all like that. I led away my horse, I led my oxen to the communal yard, I handed over my cart, my light, iron-tyred wagonette, two yokes, all my horse harness, and now, am I really alive, am I alive? I myself don't properly know. Even the daylight seems to be shining through a mist. I'm overcome with yearning, and I just can't get over it. Just think! Ever since I was a boy I've grown up among horses and bullocks, all my life I've fed myself through them, I lived right till old age with them. But now I'm left alone without a draught animal, like an old tree stump in the forest. There's no one to go out to in the yard, the yard's empty. . . . Do you realize that, my good man? No one to go out to! Or maybe you think that such grief lies on one's heart like down!

'Take only the oxen, for instance; the amount of attention they needed. In the summer, when you were harvesting, to make sure they had the strength you didn't sleep a wink all night; you pastured them, you watched over them to see they didn't stray far, to see they didn't get their food from someone else's grain. You had to work all day, and so, as you hadn't slept for so many nights, you swayed like a drunken man and held the fork in your hands by sheer force. And as soon as autumn came, and all through the winter, you had work up to your eyebrows with your oxen: every night without fail you had to go out to see to them two or three times, to give them more fodder, because the nights were long, and you couldn't put down too much hay for them at one time, otherwise they'd only trample it underfoot and eat dirty hay. And you'd got to keep enough in store to last you through till the spring. No matter how fit your oxen come through the winter, if you don't feed them properly in the spring a warm breeze will blow, and the oxen will be lying down in the furrow, and you'll be weeping bitter tears over them.

'And the horse, too, needs to be watched over strictly just the same: you must water it at the right time, and clean it, and the night before going on a journey you give it grain, or a mixture of oats and hay. And so if you're a good master you spend the nights in anxieties and activities. And so you get used to sleeping like a hare: you seem to be sleeping, but all the time you're listening, and as soon as the first cocks start crowing you haven't time to lie any longer, you've got to get up.

'During the fifty years I've been working on my farm, I've grown unused to sleeping without a break; necessity has weaned me from sleeping deep, and now I'm completely robbed of sleep. I sort of forget myself when evening comes on; but about midnight I wake up, and my sleep's gone completely, no matter how much I screw up my eyes. Last night I did doze off a little, but then I came round and thought: "Time to put some hay down for the oxen." I got up, pulled my felt boots over my bare feet, dressed, went out into the yard, and only then remembered that my oxen were in the communal yard, that an easy life had come my way. . . . And my heart was filled with such a yearning because of that easy life, it was worse than being completely helpless.'

For a long time after, even in my sleep, I heard the old man's muffled, complaining voice, and his heavy coughing. Proko-fievich woke me up just before dawn. The coals were glowing faintly through the ashes in the stove, bluish little tongues of flame flickered over them playfully. The old man was asleep as he sat on the low stool, his body resting awkwardly against the bed. His hand was still touching the lamb's back; his thick fingers, angular at the knuckles, were gently stirring and trembling.

The old man was disturbed by Prokofievich's footsteps and he turned over; but he did not change the position of his hand. It was as though even in his sleep he was afraid of parting from the lamb, that last wretched personal property, the living warmth of which still seemed, so to speak, to be linking him with his recent life as an individual farmer.

As I was returning from Stalingrad last autumn, I recalled that old man in the village of Lower Yablonovka.

Late in the night we arrived at one of the collective farms not far from Kalach. Just as in 1930, one little light in all the village drew us to a small hut at the end of the broad, grass-grown street.

There was something homely and dear to the heart in the picture I saw lit up by the dim moonlight: new white cottages, and, as though standing guard over them, pyramidal poplars shooting upwards. My driver stopped the car, and at once we were wrapped in the bitter scent of wormwood from the nearby pasturage.

Hardly had the light of our car headlamps shone over the low grey fencing when a man with a greatcoat flung round his shoulders came out on to the verandah. Narrowing his eyes against the light, limping a little, he came down the steps and shouted:

'Kolesnichenko, is that you?' Then, as he came over to the wicket gate of his yard, he said in a disillusioned tone: 'Oh, it's a car. . . . Who are you? Where've you come from?'

Our driver answered jokingly:

'You're a strict one, aren't you! We've hardly had time to halt by his gate when he puts us through an interrogation; who are you and where've you come from. He'll be demanding to see our documents next. Are they all as strict as you in this village?'

The man in the military greatcoat came to the car door and said good-naturedly:

'Well, brother, if necessary you'll show us your documents, too. I suppose you're thinking of spending the night here? Well, that's just the point: it's late, and we can't put you up anywhere else now, so you'll have to spend the night with me. But don't get annoyed about the documents: it's just a front-line habit. And besides, the local government's in my hands: I'm the chairman of the local collective farm.'

An elderly woman and two children were asleep on a broad bed in the bedroom. The woman opened her eyes just for a moment, then went off again into the deep, all-embracing sleep which marks someone really tired. The master turned up the lamp a little, and said in an undertone:

'You must excuse me, but I shan't disturb the missus, she hasn't had any sleep for three nights. She's been carting grain to the Grain Collection centre.'

The grizzled hair on the temples of his sunburnt face and the deeply carved furrows on his forehead told of a life not spent in ease.

Tiptoeing around, he brought us a jug of milk, and sat down at the table.

'Help yourselves. "What the house is rich in. . . ." '

'Have you been chairman long?' I asked.

'Since 1943. . . . As soon as I returned from the front after being wounded, I took over the chairman's job.'

Our host looked to be not less than sixty, and my driver asked in surprise.

'But how did you get to the front, daddy? They didn't take old men like you into the army.'

Our host ran his fingers over his whiskers with a dashing gesture, and smiled:

'I got there the same way as you did, my son, by the same road. True, they didn't call up my year into the army, but I couldn't stick remaining at home, and in 1942 I joined up as a volunteer. Our district committee secretary laughed at the time: "What good would you be, old man? If you were drafted into the infantry you'd be put to shame in front of the youngsters. You'd far better work as a collective farm brigadier. We need people in the rear, too." But I told him: "Laughter's out of place now, comrade secretary, when the Germans have taken so much from us already. If I go into the army it means that I'm responsible for myself. But any sensible woman can work as a brigadier; look what they're doing already.' Well, so I went. They drafted me into a sappers' company as a driver, but I asked and got transferred to the infantry. True, at my age it wasn't an easy life. Oh, far from it! But after all I was in it of my own choice, so I had to stick it. I fought at Stalingrad, and advanced as far as Kursk. But there, close to Porokhovaya, I was knocked right out. My luck was out, they'd got my number. I served one year and, d'you know, in that year I was wounded three times. And I'm not exactly young in years, you know.'

Out host grew perceptibly more animated, and began talking rather louder:

'Youngsters even heal from wounds without trouble, they're just like young trees. But it's harder for an old man. That I know very well from my own experience. After my second wound I was in hospital at Tambov, and among us there were men who'd lost a leg. The older ones didn't want particularly to live, they lay all jaundiced with themselves, frowning. All night they did nothing but sigh and groan, all you heard was the beds creaking under them as they turned over and over, wondering what life would be like for them as cripples and how they'd manage to keep their families. When that's the sort of night thoughts you have, you don't get a lot of cheerful ideas, you've got to realize that. But the youngsters, what did they worry about? Of course they grieved terribly to themselves, but they never showed any sign of it. One of them would wake up in the morning, and he'd find there were no crutches for him – there weren't enough to go all round – but you watched him, and you'd see him get hold of the bed-head, grope along the wall with his hands and go hopping along the corridor on one leg, like a sparrow, and singing a gay love song into the bargain! That's what youth means! You'd look at him and feel sorry for him, yet you couldn't help feeling envious, you'd think to yourself: "Ah, if only I could knock twenty or thirty years off my life! Then perhaps I'd go hopping along as well as he does, like a sparrow."

'They'd bring in some youngster quite seriously wounded;

and yet in a couple of weeks you'd see him, that son of a devil, winking at the nurse, making eyes at her, sighing like a horse and pulling a thousand faces such as I at my age, for instance, was quite incapable of! You'd keep an eye on him from your bed, and you'd be surprised. But they'd bring in some elderly soldier, and he'd lie there, going all sour with lying. He'd pester the doctors and the nurses and get thoroughly fed up with himself; and yet his wound wouldn't be all that serious. All the same, he'd lie there getting more and more bored, staring up at the ceiling, occupying a bed in the hospital to no purpose.

'Still all the same it has to be said: we elderly men got involved in this war because we simply had to: the enemy wanted to strip us clean of everything we'd accumulated under our régime. And you've got to realize that. . . .

'In my case I had one little bone shattered by a shell fragment, and it took a long time to knit again. I'd ask the doctor: "Why is this bone of mine so slow in knitting together? It looks as if you haven't put the cast on properly." But he'd ask me: "How old are you?" "Fifty-six." And he'd laugh: "You're just the right age for getting married, that's why it's so slow in knitting. But if you should get wounded in twenty years' time, say, your bone will hardly knit together at all." "Why," I'd think, "what are you thinking of, damn you? Will I still be fighting in twenty years' time? What good will that do?"

' "No, comrade doctor," I answered him, "I thank you most humbly, but I've got to finish off the Fascists rather quicker than that, first because they've peppered me rather badly, and then because I'm not of an age to go mucking about with them for any length of time. And besides, what sort of soldier will I make in twenty years' time? I'd be a walking shame, not a soldier. I'll have to give myself my own discharge; my platoon commander won't bother to ask where private so-and-so has got to. He'll be only too glad to get rid of me."

'Only it was quite impossible to talk with that joking doctor. He'd just laugh and say: "What are you worried about, Kornei Vasilievich? We're the doctors and everything's in our hands. And in twenty years' time if anything happens to you we'll patch you up so perfectly that you won't lose a single grain, and you'll go about as bravely as a young cockerel, with both head and tail up!"

'I lay there a couple of months and got well again. But at Kursk I got a worse packet.'

And, as though seeking to justify himself, he added:

'But what do you think? Could I refuse to go and fight such an enemy? Think of the life he'd disturbed, that blasted enemy! Before the war our collective farm had three lorries, two schools, a club, a mill, we had everything in plenty: grain and every other good thing. But when he passed over our district everything went up in smoke. He destroyed everything, the creeping reptile!

'When I got back here in 1943 I clutched my head: the Fritz devils had burnt down half the village, and the rest of the houses they'd ruined by using them as gun nests. They'd burnt down the schools, and out of one hundred and eighty yoke of oxen only two yoke were left, and not a single horse. They'd damaged the tractors and put them out of service. And so we had to start all over again.

'There were only women and children working in the fields. Only green young girls on the tractors! I could say it was a joke! To give you one instance: in the spring I was walking across the fields and saw a tractor standing with its engine running. But there wasn't a sign of the driver or her assistant. "Now what's up?" I wondered. "Where have they got to?" I walked along to the wood, and there they were both sitting up in a willow, robbing a rook of her eggs. They weren't even sixteen; they still thought like children, so what could you do with them? But what sort of work did they do? I tell you it was beyond all belief. Turning over the engine of a cold tractor – no matter how much you warm it up – is not an easy job, we'll agree. Well, you go walking round the fields, and the girl tractor driver would come running a mile or more after you, stumbling over the furrows: "Daddy Kornei Vasilievich, come and start it up! I haven't got the strength." But do you realize what it meant for a girl to handle such a machine? They've got tender bellies, it was quite easy for one to over-strain herself. Even with our sturdy male frame it makes the joints crack at times.

228

'But the women, the dears! My God, as you watched them working on the collective farm it well nigh broke your heart. And yet they not only had to work on the farm but manage all their domestic work, cleaning up their homes after dark, looking after the children and grieving over their husbands who were away fighting. The woman had to manage everything; but you couldn't refashion the work to suit her small hands, nor could you change her bitter thoughts.

'One day I was out in the fields, it was before dawn, but my woman neighbour was already mowing hay for her cow before going off to the collective farm work. Her husband had been killed, she had four small children – the smallest, a baby – to look after. I went over to give her a hand, and her eyes gave me such a sombre look that, you wouldn't believe it, I came to a stop and lit a cigarette. And all through the war I never smoked, even in the worst of times. I kept off it. But now I rolled a cigarette and smoked, she gripped my heart so hard with that sombre look.'

Meditatively tapping his fingers on the table, he said;

'We've got an old woman's song:

> *'Ah, no one suffers so much*
> *As my darling at the war.*
> *He himself loads the cannon,*
> *He himself is thinking of me.'*

And a youthful, merry smile seemed to light up my host's face.

'They've got a good opinion of themselves, have our women. And they're quite right, too. There's no denying it, when we were fighting we thought of them day and night. Of course there were times, in the heat of the battle, when for a little while you forgot everything. But then you flew back home again in your thoughts.

'When I came back from the front I looked about me to see how people were working at home, and it struck me to the heart that the burden on these women's shoulders was identical with what we were enduring at the front.

'While I was at the front I received a present. Nothing out of the ordinary: an embroidered tobacco pouch, rusks and other things, and a little note. A woman worker in a Moscow works had written it: "Dear fighter, I send you a present and a hearty greeting: beat the enemy as he deserves. We are working day and night on defence, but in spirit we are with you." Well, and she finished up as usual, wishing me good health.

'And this arrived just at the difficult time of the battle for Kursk. The German tanks came on in a black cloud, we threw them back as ordered, there was no let-up in the fighting, after it was over you were amazed to find you were still alive. And then this present arrived. I was handed it right in the front-line trenches; and you know, I cried. . . . As I said, I'm not a smoker myself, I didn't need the pouch. But of course I ate the biscuits, and as I ate my salty tears dropped on them. Well, I thought, there's a working woman who, like us, doesn't sleep day or night. She's working for us at the front, and yet she's remembered me. And perhaps she had to make some sacrifice for it? Because of my thoughts those biscuits were all the sweeter.'

He smiled and touched his grizzled whiskers with his fingers.

'And yet, you know, even that had a funny side to it. She'd sent it thinking it might fall into a young man's hands. But it came to an old man.

'Our women did a great job during the war. And they worked with great conscientiousness; they realized how necessary their work was to the Soviet régime. That's how I see it with my old brain, I think they've earned a monument to themselves.'

An hour later I was awakened by the noise of a lorry engine. My host's voice reached me from the kitchen:

'Why are you so late in arriving, Kolesnichenko? You ought to have been here long ago. Have we got to keep the tractor standing waiting on your pleasure? I can see you've got a poor conscience. I don't need you to tell me the lorry tyres are bad. You've got to be clever enough to drive on poor tyres; anyone can drive on good ones. Take the fuel out to the fields at once, and tell Semion I'll be coming out at dawn.'

The master groped his way in the darkness to his bed and, groaning and grunting as an old man does, began to undress.

A little time later I was again disturbed by a hard blow on the window. A hoarse masculine voice called loudly from outside:

'Kornei Vasilievich, the wagons of the second brigade have arrived. Are they to load up with the grain at once or wait till the morning? The oxen have got terribly tired.'

The master went to the window and said quietly:

'Let them load up and take the grain away at once. Wait a bit! I'll come out, and we'll go together to the granaries.'

I did not hear when he returned; but long before dawn he was aroused again: one of the tractors doing the autumn ploughing had broken down, and my host went to the collective farm office to phone the motor traction station. He was disturbed three more times that night. Just before daylight came our driver, who had failed to get a good sleep, sighed bitterly and said:

'Well, daddy, you live a gay life. . . . Spending the night with you is like sleeping in a club with the music going all the time.'

Our host, who was already dressed, smiled wearily and said:

'We live a restless sort of life. We've got a large farm, there's lots to do, and so we have to work at night, too. But now you can get some proper rest, there won't be any more disturbance, I'm going out. We've got a meeting of the collective farm administration.'

I looked at my watch; it was half past four.

My driver roared with laughter.

'Who on earth starts a meeting at five in the morning?'

'Well, what do you think, my son? During the day all the administration members are out in the fields; one is unloading the grain, another is in the field crops brigade, a third is going to Stalingrad to obtain spare parts for a machine and I must get out to the fields at dawn as well. And so we decided to hold our meeting earlier, and to discuss our affairs briefly. All of us have only one thought: how we can most quickly put the collective farm on its feet. We have no intention of living any worse than others!

'And besides, it would be shameful for us to live worse than others, because the State's giving us a lot of help. Not to mention other kinds of machinery, our district has received more than thirty caterpillar tractors this year. You've got to realize that too! But things are rapidly improving. This year the harvest is very good, we've ploughed much more land this autumn than last, and our collective farm has sown some four hundred hectares more with winter wheat.

'If we managed to get through such a great disaster as last year's drought there'll be no stopping us now. That's certain.'

'So the drought hit you, too, did it?' our driver asked with interest.

'It did, my son, and how! But it didn't knock us off our feet. We stand firm on our land! I think that if we were to have a drought like those of the old days, half the people would die off. Why, how did the peasantry live in those times? One man would swell with hunger, and another, because he was rich, would have granaries full of grain, but he wouldn't lift a finger to help his neighbour. And in those days the government didn't think the people's misery was anything to do with it. But now it's a different story. We ran into trouble with last year's drought, but the State got us out of it, it helped with grain and seed. We gave food to those who were weaker, we supported them as best we could. And so they survived. And the people saved everything.

'But when the spring came, how we worked! We've got some members who're bowled over in the wind, but all the same, they went out into the fields and worked with all their strength. We've got a wonderful lot of people, you've got to realize that, too.'

We drove out of that village at sunrise. In the street was the sweet tender scent of goosefoot. A raw cold wind was blowing from the Don. The heavy clouds were floating so low that they looked as if at any moment they would be caught by their rosily tipped wings on the bare crowns of the lofty poplars.

Despite the early hour, there was great activity and hubbub around the collective farm granaries. Two old men were sifting grain through a riddle; at the end granary about a dozen wagons, evidently arrived from the farm threshing floor, were unloading. Here there was also a two-ton lorry, and a tall driver in a quilted coat, completely unbuttoned, and a fur cap thrust to the back of his head was furiously pumping up a tyre, at the same time soundlessly but expressively moving his lips.

Some two miles outside the village, not far from the road a brand new tractor, with the letters S.T.Z. NATI not yet burnt off its body, was at work. Behind it a man in a military greatcoat was walking with a limp; he was bending down from time to time, measuring the depth of the furrow with a twig.

My driver pointed merrily to him, and smiled:

'There he is, our chairman, hopping along the furrow like a rook. He's strong, is that lame old devil! I bet the tractor driver won't plough shallow and won't make any mistakes while he's around. Before we left I went to ask the way. Out of curiosity I had a look at the granaries. The grain they've got stored, oho! And the people are very satisfied with their Kornei Vasilievich. "He's a bit strict," they say, "is our old man. But as a farmer he's first-rate. He's always just. And the work here goes well, because he has respect for us, and we for him." I started grumbling about him: "We put up with the master for the night, but we had nothing but disturbance all the time. He himself didn't sleep all night because of the farm, and he didn't let us have any either." But one old gaffer laughed: "Yes, he's a restless sort. But water doesn't flow under motionless stones. If he hadn't been so restless our farm wouldn't have recovered in these past two years." '

As he stood admiring the splendid winter wheat running in broad green waves away to the horizon, my driver added:

'That's the collective farm wheat. What a fine crop they've grown! During the night that Kornei Vasilievich was always talking about the people. But when the people are good and the one who directs them is good the result's beautiful!'

Taking up the chairman's own words, he added:

'And you've got to realize that too!'

1948

Sunlight and Shadow

The warm May breezes are blowing over the fabulous expanses of our great Mother Country, the white, smokily fringed clouds are floating in our gracious spring sky; washed by the first life-giving rains, radiant with sunlight, the bushy winter wheat is looking amazingly green over the endless collective farm fields, and already the thick, even shoots of the spring crop are showing through and avidly stretching up to the light, greedily acquiring new strength.

But over all the boundless expanse, from Guriev to Ismailia and from Orsk to Tula, the spring saw the opening of an attack on the evil forces of nature – the greatest attack in history – on drought and the burning winds; and with all the might peculiar only to our Soviet people a titanic struggle has developed to transform nature, to realize to the full the plans sketched out by the Party.

Many thousands of tractors from the motor and tractor parks, the Soviet farms and the only recently created forestry protection stations, many tens of thousands of collective farm draught horses, oxen and camels have ploughed up the first hundreds of thousands of hectares destined for afforestation; and in the deep furrows, on the fields and in the arboretums, adequately covered with soil which still retains its vital, cheerful spring coolness, the acorns are still patiently awaiting germination and their emergence into the world, the first seedlings of the future state oaks, and the seeds of ash and maple, of elms and birches, limes and larches, honeysuckle, acacia and tamarisk.

Over the bare, everlastingly mournful sand dunes of the trans-Don basin, in the dreary and lifeless expanses of sand beyond the Volga and Stavropol, for thousands of years the murderous sands have crept on from the east irresistibly, invulnerably, year by year engulfing more and more of the fertile soil with their insatiable yellow maw. But now the ploughs have turned up the first furrows, and at their bottoms, where the heavy iron dibber of the tree-planter plunged into the burning sand, little pine seedlings are lurking between the clods, as though clinging to the damp sand, and have flourished marvellously, covering the soil with green splashes of malachite. They are only one year old, and must be two before they are strong; but go down on your knees in the fiery heat of noon, bend over the tiny trees, and your nostrils will catch the young and tender scent of pine resin; and on the trunk-stalk, toylike, slender, shaggy and flexible, you will see tiny droplets of resin, the size of a pinhead, incommensurably large by comparison with the stalk and sparkling like dew. So the tiny pine has taken; it is living, it will live, for many long years keeping unchanging guard, defending the fortunes and the happiness of our fields of black earth against the irruption of the death-dealing desert.

And in sober truth, if you stand up and look at the pine seedlings from a distance, at their rows and rows ranging with soldierly precision away to the horizon and seemingly drowning in the yellow mirage, with the broken soil separating them at regular intervals, you involuntarily think that they resemble our frontier guards not only by the protective colouring of their 'headgear' and 'uniforms' but also by their noble community of tasks. True, at present these sand 'frontier guards' are still small, but not all that amount of water will flow down the swift Ural river, down the majestic Volga and the gentle Don – only a few calculable years will pass – before the young pines rise to a sturdy, soldierly size. They will be the first to bear the ruthless blows of the savage trans-Caspian sandstorms, and they will stand fast!

But they also have assistants; spaced out into the heart of the land, from the Caspian to the Black Sea, innumerable ribbons of forest seedlings extend over the black earth of the fields and the steppes. Planted and reared by the careful and talented hands of the true husbandmen of the earth, they have ranged their sticky, lanceted leaves over the south of the country. The May wind is rustling them tenderly, teaching them the gift of speech; and their first, barely audible, gentle rustling is as dear to the heart of every man as the first prattle of an infant.

235

The air of our Mother Country is quivering with the roar of the mighty tractors passing over the earth. From the Baltic to the Pacific Ocean, from the Arctic to the Pamirs, everywhere that roar, peaceful but expressive of restrained and heavy strength, is to be heard. Day and night the tractors are at work. Submissive to the will of men who were formerly tank crews and are now efficient young drivers, they plough, sow, harrow, haul timber to the ports and quays, shift earth for the industrial plants and new construction works, make roads and drag the tree-planting machinery. And there is not one corner of our land where the Soviet people, as they listen to the incessant roar of the engines, will not think with all a son's unfading sorrow and burning gratitude of the greatest of the great, of him who at one time dreamed only of one hundred thousand tractors for Soviet Russia, of him who created the Party and the Soviet state, and who incarnated in living reality the hopes of many generations of toilers.

A still, chilly night. In the profound, deep blue vault of the sky not one little cloud is to be seen, only the moon on its back almost in the zenith, and from horizon to horizon the glimmering sprinkle of fine vernal stars above our native steppe.

It is hard going across the furrows of the tractor which is ploughing in the night; one moment you stumble over the furrow, then your foot slips off the tight, dully gleaming layer of black earth polished by the share, then you are caught in the outstretched string of roots of a steppe weed. The young moon sheds a dim light, and only close at hand can one see the black clods, shining like anthracite, of the soil loosened after years of lying fallow. Beyond, all around you everything is lost in mist, in a vague and spectral haze.

From underfoot rises the fresh dampness of the newly up-turned earth and the sharp and perhaps very slightly mournful scent of the young grass smitten by the plough. A quail, which has only recently flown in from beyond the warm sea, beats out, speaks out still uncertainly and monotonously in the unmown grass of last year: 'I want to sleep, I want to sleep.' But no, the steppe does not sleep. At the top of the gully a powerful tractor is raising Maytime vapours as it drags two five-shared ploughs.

Its deep roar covers the noise of a lighter tractor working not far away, in the neighbouring field. Now the S. 80 has turned with a clatter at the end of the furrow, and the gentle breath of the western wind has reinforced and, one would think, brought much closer the thunderous, rolling roar of its engine. One can distinctly hear the furious scream and rattle of its caterpillars as they crush the stones beneath them, and the driver's voice shouting something to his assistant at the plough.

Bluish sparks from under the caterpillar tracks, an orange flame from the vertical exhaust pipe and then again the tractor's measured advance, the phosphorescent light of the headlamps slipping over the ground. Lit up by them, the exuberant white foam of a flowering hawthorn momentarily raises a dazzling flame in the distance, then slowly fades, withdraws into the haze.

Not far from the edge of the ploughed land a little light shines welcomingly in the window of the tractor brigade's wagon. My companion, a mechanic from the motor-tractor park, and I go up to the wagon. A little way off, behind a table with legs thrust into the ground, the brigade cook is washing up utensils. Evidently a shift has only just had supper. To one side, close to a water barrel, a broad-shouldered tractor driver, bare to the waist, is washing, blissfully grunting and snorting; a second man is pouring water copiously from a bucket into the first man's outstretched palms and over his bent neck. The one who is washing suddenly cries out in alarm, spluttering and coughing, and says in a quivering tenor:

'Fiodya, pour it more carefully over my neck. I ask you kindly. The water's from the spring, it's like ice, but you're pouring it down my back. Are you blind, or did you do it on purpose? You'll give me a cold, blast you! Why, it's running down my spine right to my feet, and I'm all sweating. Do you understand, you beast?'

Fiodya's rather hollow rumbling bass answers ruthlessly:

'I expect at the front you rubbed yourself down with snow of a morning, didn't you? Well then, you can stand this water. I reckon you ought to stand it: you've got a backbone like an artillery horse.'

'But that was in the army. . . . And my backbone's got nothing to do with it. That's enough, I don't want any more,' the gasping tenor voice pleads, turning at once to threats: 'Put the bucket down or I'll give you a bath head-first in the barrel.'

We stop by the wagon to light up and smoke. Behind us we hear laughter, a healthy-sounding smack on a bare body, the clatter of a bucket dropped and the rapid, retreating patter of four feet.

'Ah, these youngsters!' the elderly mechanic sighs for some reason. 'The devils don't know what tiredness is. And I admit they need to stretch their legs after sitting all day on a tractor.'

A minute or so later something heavy smacks down hard on the ploughland. A brief scuffle, laughter, heavy breathing and then Fiodya's bass sounding as if it is coming from under the ground:

'Vaska, stop it, or you'll crush me to death. Oh, damn it, I heard something crack in my loins. . . . Let me go, you stupid clot. You've got the strength of a horse. . . . You'll crush me.'

Although the door is wide open, blue tobacco smoke is floating in the wagon. The place has the smell of recently washed pine floors, home-grown tobacco and the ineradicable smell of paraffin and cabbage soup. Seated around the table and on the bunks are the tractor drivers and their assistants of the first shift, the tractor brigadier, Trifon Platonovich, an old collective farmer who is now a fuel-tanker driver, the book-keeper and two other collective farmers from the field cultivation brigade, who have come on a friendly visit to the tractor brigade, to have a 'communal smoke'.

Shifting an old issue of the magazine *Ogoniok* closer to the lamp, the book-keeper reads:

'If the future forest strips were to be extended in a single unbroken ribbon thirty yards wide, it would go round the earth at the equator over fifty times; ten to fifteen per cent of the protective forest plantations will consist of fruit trees and bushes, and that will mean a further seven hundred thousand hectares of fruit orchard.'

The strict silence is suddenly broken by old Trifon, who can't be restrained: he bangs his fist so hard on the table that the lamp jumps and the yellow tongue of flame shoots out above the glass, and cries exultantly:

'May you sit on a hedgehog! Now that's an orchard for you! I'm too old to know anything about those "equators" and what-not they're talking about; but seven hundred thousand hectares of orchard: that, my boys . . . at the moment I can't take it in with my mind, either, but, my boys, it's a great benefit!'

Someone laughs. But the brigadier says sternly:

'Use your fist a little more gently, old man; sit still and listen in silence!'

'What do you mean by "sit in silence"?' Trifon asks indignantly. 'Things like that are being read out to us, and you tell me to be silent?'

The book-keeper, a youngster in a faded tunic, gives the old fellow a reproachful look, turns up the wick and continues:

'On the restored earth forty-four thousand ponds will be brought into existence. . . .'

And again old Trifon cannot control himself; crumpling his grey beard in his fist, he says in a voice that rumbles all through the wagon:

'Forty-four thousand! Our minds can't grasp that, brothers.'

This time everybody laughs. Growing interested, the mechanic asks:

'Who wrote that article?'

Without looking up at him the book-keeper answers:

'The head of all the afforestation strips, comrade Chekmeniev.' Narrowing his eyes and staring at the fidgety old Trifon, he says abruptly: 'Daddy Platonovich, you've left the oxen with no one to look after them, and now I expect they're the other side of Stony Gully. You should go and see where they are. Who knows: they may get right away. And we'll be left without fuel.'

The old man rumbles this simple trick, and answers without taking offence:

'Read on, read on! I know all about my oxen, you needn't worry about them. You're young to try and catch an old sparrow with chaff. Read on, and don't squint at me!'

With a sigh, the book-keeper reads:

'The destructive ulcers of the steppe, the ravines, will disappear. The menacing black storms will die out. Drought will be banished, the climate will grow milder, moister and man's

239

life in the steppe incomparably more comfortable, lighter, finer and richer. The collective and Soviet farms will gather stable harvests, progressively increasing, of grain, fruit and vegetables. On the luxuriant pasturages fat herds of large-horned cattle and fine-fleeced sheep will graze. That is what the transformation of nature will bring the Soviet people.'

For a little while everybody is thoughtfully silent. Even old Trifon, the most garrulous member of this little collective in the heart of the steppe, is silent. The book-keeper, a youngster who has seen the world, having marched during the war all the way to Prague, and come back disabled, drums on the clean scrubbed board of the table with bent fingers and, half-closing his eyelids, smiles dreamily. With misted eyes he is seeing his native land not scarred and wounded by war, but adorned in luxuriant green foliage.

The general mood and the silence are again disturbed by old Trifon. He raises one hand, black and as gnarled as a root, and says:

'Stop, lads! Don't read any more, Mikish! Tomorrow, when I get back with fuel late in the afternoon we'll discuss this article together and look at the other pictures. But now we've got to consider this business.'

'What is there to consider? It's all quite clear, it's fine. You're too used to letting your tongue wag, old man,' the brigadier says discontentedly; he has had no liking for old Trifon for a long time past.

The old fellow calmly objects:

'I'm not a rag to wipe a wheel with and not a thin mitten to be wagged about. I want to speak to the point. How can you say there's nothing to consider? You don't see anything beyond your tractors, you've got stuck in them. But here we've got to get everything clear in advance, everything down to the last thread.'

'Well, what have we got to get clear?' one of the tractor assistants asks impatiently.

In addition to all his other virtues old Trifon is a sceptic: he maintains a significant silence, sweeps an anxious gaze round the others, then asks in an ominous whisper:

'But how about the finance department?'

'What finance department? What's the finance department got do with it?' the brigadier asks in his turn, staring at him in bewilderment.

Going crimson with laughter, the tractor driver Nikonov says:

'All you're fit for, daddy Trifon, is to be the Minister for War in America. There's something about you that's quite like him, the way you start to talk. You don't happen to be him, by any chance, do you? Your mind isn't touched, is it?'

'If it was touched there'd have been no windows in your wagon long ago, and I'd have long since been without trousers no worse than that minister: I'd have been tossing about the ploughlands like a skinny mongrel at market. And we shall yet see which of us two is the stupider and the more suitable for the ministerial post in America,' the old man answered good-temperedly. Turning to the brigadier, he fired at him: 'You ask what the finance department's got to do with it. Just this: last year I was summoned to the village Soviet, and an agent of the finance department asks me: "How many trees are there in your orchard, grand-dad?" "How the hell should I know?" I answered, "Go and count them for yourself." He didn't mind; commissions arrived and counted every tree, and the financial department agent says: "Every tree with stones, like the plum and suchlike, four of them are to be reckoned as one-hundredth of taxable land; and every seed fruit tree, an apple or a pear, each tree counts as one-hundredth." "That," I told him, "is beyond all understanding; how d'you get that? On the one hand, we receive instructions to develop our orchards, and on the other we've got to pay for every tree. And I get as much benefit from those trees as milk from a goat; they don't even bear a fig. I'm already wondering whether to chop some of them down."'

A voice comes from a bunk in a twilit corner:

'Come to the point, daddy!'

'That is the point! At first I was delighted when I heard of seven hundred thousand orchards and about the ponds. But then I was dumbfounded. Well, the ponds are a different matter; you can't put a tax on carp, you can only scrape the scales off them. But orchards. . . . Here, my lads, you've got to think it out right to the end. Supposing in Moscow the very highest minister of the finance department, what's his name. . . . I've forgotten it, God grant me memory. . . . But I read it in the paper only the other day, and I fixed it in my head. . . .'

'Zveriev?' the book-keeper prompted him.

'That's it, that's the name. And supposing this comrade Zveriev thinks up the idea of putting a tax on all the seven hundred thousand orchards, what then? For you'll have either fruit with stones or fruit with pips in them. They won't be twisted elms or buck-thorns with warts.'

'What a darned wrecker you are, daddy Trifon!' the book-keeper exclaimed irritably, angrily closing the periodical. 'You're always thinking up some nonsense or other, spoiling everything. . . .'

Obviously offended, the old man rose to his full height, which was considerable, and his voice thundered under the low ceiling of the wagon:

'And what have I thought up that's harmful? I simply said that this question has to be understood properly and discussed from all angles. And what are you trying to stop my mouth for – may you sit on a hedgehog! Am I any worse at understanding things than you? Seventy-two years I've lived, and do I understand things worse? I should say not! What I say is this: we ought to send a letter to comrade Zveriev from our collective farm and ask him what he thinks of all these orchards, and would he tell us quickly, without any blarney and quite frankly, what tax he thinks of putting on them. He'll write back sincerely, and that will be to the point. If the tax is an average one carry on, boys, plant both pip and stone trees.'

'We'll manage it without any letter,' one of the tractor drivers says resolutely. 'We'll gather fruit from the afforested strips, and so we'll be able to pay the tax. It won't ruin us, and there's no need to hum and hah over it. You're used to thinking as if it was the old days, daddy.'

'Go to the devil!' the offended old man thunders, finally losing all patience. Pulling down his jerkin by its sleeve from a bunk, he flings it round his shoulders and makes for the door.

At the door he collides with two belated tractor drivers. By the vast breadth of his shoulders one of them is easily recognizable as Vasily, and the other is evidently Fiodya. Fiodya has dashingly twisted whiskers and humorous black eyes. Stepping aside to let the old man stalk past, he says in his rumbling bass:

'Someone upset Trifon Platonovich again? I suppose he had another of his crack-brained ideas, and you upset him? He's so angry you can almost see the smoke puffing out of his nose.'

'You stupid whelp, look where you're going!' the old man says and goes out, slamming the door behind him.

Fiodya smiles and winks at me:

'It's never boring here. We haven't got a cinema, but the old man is just as good. He's a terrible one for splitting hairs, he's got a nail for every hole. There's never a conversation but he must join in.'

With a grunt the brigadier takes off his boots, wipes them diligently with an oily rag and, raising his head, remarks:

'The tax is just an ordinary trifle; the main thing is will all the various Trumans allow us to complete the great work of returning nature to the right path? Look how mad they've gone with their preparations for war, and with such industry that their ministers are going out of their minds with the strain!'

'But are you really afraid of war?' the mechanic smiled.

'What the devil have I got to be afraid of? Let them be afraid! "Us they wanted to defeat, to defeat us they made ready."'

'"But we weren't afraid of them, we were waiting for them,"' someone's deep bass sang out from a distant corner of the bunks.

'The people who're afraid are those whose heels are scarified with fear, who jump out of the window without their trousers, like that Forrestal. But my job would be quite a small one: to get on my tank and give it them the same as we did the Fritzes.' The brigadier smiled and screwed up his eyes. 'And what fine machines we've turned out since the war!'

A collective farmer who had not previously spoken asked irresolutely:

'But why have they gone in for all this in America? What has that trouserless minister jumped out of the window for? I haven't heard anything about it.'

'He got it into his stupid head one night that the Red Army

243

had invaded America, and so he jumped out of the window naked,' the mechanic condescendingly explained. 'We know these fighters! They make big threats, but they can't contain themselves, and their trousers won't stay up without braces. There was a clot like that during the Civil War, who threatened to kill off all the Bolsheviks. Well, we thought we'd try him out, to see what guts he'd really got! One night in the winter our regimental reconnaissance unit galloped into the district centre of Ust-Khopersk, and he was asleep there, drunk with his staff. He wasn't expecting such welcome guests! And he didn't have time to pull on his trousers either. He galloped twenty miles on his horse through the frost only in his drawers. And then they couldn't catch up with him, the son of a bitch!'

'The poor devil must have got badly frost-bitten, I suppose,' Fiodya asked with hyprocritical sympathy.

'But I never had a chance to ask his wife about that.' The mechanic waved his hand, and began pulling off his boots to the accompaniment of a roar of laughter.

As they prepared for bed they talked for some time longer about the successes of the Chinese army of national liberation, the world congress in defence of peace, the situation in Indonesia, the weather and of how at the moment they were outstripping the next district in Socialist competition, but it wasn't at all certain how the harvest would turn out. Gradually the voices died away.

I went out of the wagon. The moon had faded, and the stars seemed to have grown larger. That measured roar of tractor engines still sounded over the steppe. But above Stony Gully, where a dense growth of thorn bushes was foaming with exuberant blossom, I heard the jugging, enchanting patter of a nightingale's trills.

1949

New Year Greetings, Fellow Countrymen

On the eve of a new year which starts the second half of our century, we recall as always what our immortal Lenin said at the turn of the century, when he was creating the majestic Party to which the heroic Russian working class gave birth.

'Before us in all its might stands the enemy fortress from which we are showered with clouds of shot and bullets, carrying off our finest fighters. We must capture that fortress, and we *shall* capture it. . . .'

In our country that fortress has been captured. We have created a new, shining world. These fortresses have also been captured in the countries of the people's democracies, which are building a new life. The great Chinese nation, our brother in arms, has taken the radiant road. We shall wait for the toiling people to take all the fortresses everywhere. The dark forces will not prove an invincible barrier. The people will conquer! We believe that; we struggle whole-heartedly and we shall live for ever; behind us is the joyous life which we have created with our own hands.

My dear compatriots, comrades, friends, will greet the coming year with even stronger faith in the victory of Communist ideas.

The second half of the century is arriving.

There is a bright future for all humanity. There will be a morning with a clear sky. . . . The mother will awaken, the child in the cradle will awaken and no one will remember that there were ever MacArthurs and Trumans in the world.

Through my own native steppe flows the Volga–Don canal. A great irrigation system is being created. With their gigantic construction works the Bolsheviks are transforming the face of the whole Soviet land. It is joyful to live and create, as a son of the great Mother Country, a son of such a great Party.

New Year greetings, fellow countrymen.

December 31st, 1950

Dear Mother–Fatherland

The expanses of our native country are covered with a bluish, wintry haze; mists are passing over the majestic mountain ranges with their proud summits everlastingly striving upward, over the ancient seas and oceans which wash the native shores of the Fatherland. Our fields, cultivated and cherished by the toiling hands of the Soviet people, are wrapped in a moist, graciously gentle mist. Every blade of the winter wheat is gleaming with a fine frostiness, with silvery beads; each layer of soil turned over by the plough is polished with a raven steeliness.

And at this moment, somewhere in the south, doubtless the branches of the white acacia, scorched with the first frost, are chilled and trembling under the wild December wind, and in the west the branches of the pines and firs are bending low, as though burdened with memories; and at sunrise and sunset, when the slanting rays wander gropingly over the forests, the oozings of resin gleam like tears on the trunks of the still living trees slashed by bullets and shell fragments.

And in this winter night it would seem that there are only the mews above the bottomless depths of our seas and oceans, only the hawks soaring above the snow-covered sea of collective farm fields, only the call of the eagle above the lofty spurs of our inaccessible mountains.

And it would seem that the earth, the age-old giver of food, has died into silence, is lost in thought, and, in the silence, like a future mother, is gathering her vital forces for new achievements.

But this new year silence is only a seeming silence. Not for one second does the powerful rhythmic pulse of the land of socialism slacken or weaken. The gulls welcome and accompany our ships which are cleaving the waters of all the world's oceans. The implements of those who are investigating and winning coal, oil and ore for the mother country are not silenced in the womb of the earth. The 'black gold' is flowing copiously along the broad arteries of the country, feeding the mighty industry of our native land. New construction works are rising, and coming into production; and the hawk describes its circles in the crystally clear, frosty air not above unpopulated tracts of green winter corn, but where, in the socialistic fields, the hands of workers who do not know what weariness is are already firmly setting up snowbreaks, to prevent the first snows from settling uselessly in the ravines.

The mighty brood of the Soviet people has long since taken wing; and the luminous shadow of those wings covers the earthly globe, bringing freedom to all humanity suffering under the oppression of capitalism.

On the threshold of a new year, on the threshold of the edifice of Communism now under construction, our toiling people are standing on guard for peace with the rolled-up sleeves of the workers, the real masters of the earth. They extend those work-loving hands to all those who, honest in conscience and heart, are fighting and will fight in the future for the freedom and happiness of the toilers. With a cold smile of contempt, with undying hatred and with a consciousness of their own invincible might, they are keenly watching those who are incautiously playing with the fire of war.

Peace has not been taken from those whose hands held the weapons and whose inflamed lips dried the tears on the cheeks of orphaned children, whose eyes saw the horrors of the past war and for ever imprinted those horrors in their memories.

Peace and the future are ours for ever! New Year greetings, great toiler, our dear and beloved Mother–Fatherland to our last breath!

December 31st, 1951

The First-born of the Great Construction Works

On both sides of the road from Rostov-on-Don to the settlement of Tsimlansk the grain is rippling like water in flood. You cannot take it all in, you cannot comprehend it with your rejoicing eye. You gaze at it, but cannot gaze your fill. You realize with your mind that all you have seen on your journey of nearly two hundred miles is only a tiny part of the harvest wealth of the country, and yet that part which arises before your eyes appears to be boundless. Just so, in your distant childhood, that little corner of the world in which you were living seemed enormous and unsurveyable.

And on this hazy day, only occasionally brightened with sunlight, how greatly are the colours softened, colours which as a rule are southern sharp, and which in July nature scatters with spendthrift generosity! In the distance, beyond the line of burial tumuli, a thundercloud stands in the north-east half of the sky. A rainbow stretches up from the earth, but it is not strong enough to pierce the sombre black density of the cloud, it stands on the horizon with short upright columns, important and almost colourless.

The roadsides are fringed with the ashen blue of wormwood, the former mournful hue of the Don steppes. Almost everywhere it has been supplanted by grain, which powerfully, masterfully advances to the very edges of the roads; and all that is bitterly left to it is, perhaps, to live out its life only on the collective farm pasturages, on the by-roads and over the edges and slopes of the forest ravines. Immediately beyond the wormwood rises the little bluish-green wall of a hundred hectares of ripening oats, and, farther still, the vague yellowish-brown patches of belatedly ripening barley or wheat. Farther still, there is an endless brush of sunflowers, and then suddenly the heavily frozen waves of winter wheat, borne down and laid by the winds, gleam a ruddy gold under the sun. Two motor combines strain and creep through it, and sunny glints play on their dark grey sides.

Here the steppe is uneven; but very distant to the eye the fringe of the horizon is just barely visible.

At the very bottom of a broad depression the misty blue deepens; on the farther side of the slope it passes into melting lilac smoke, and on the ridge, some twelve miles from the road, at a point imperceptible to the eye it blends with the sky. Only one majestic guardian mound marks with its foot the invisible line of the horizon.

On the right bank of the middle Don there are many such guardian burial mounds. Like an ancient frontier they stand along the heights of the Don, as though surveying and guarding the trans-Don forest and steppe, whence at one time the raiders and warriors of the Khazars, the Pechenegs and the Polovtsians invaded ancient Rus. Down the centuries the hordes of foreign invaders moved on from the south-east along the left banks of the Tanais–Don rivers, and as landmarks along their routes they left the tumuli as inviolable memorials to the ancient times.

The ancient Khazar fortress of Sarkel, which was shattered even as early as the time of Sviatoslav, has been flooded by the waters of the Tsimlansk sea. And a strange feeling takes possession of you, and for some reason you feel a clutch at the throat, when from the Kumshatska hills you see not the former, long familiar, narrow ribbon of the Don winding capriciously through the green of forests and meadows, but a blue-grey expanse of water.

But our greetings to you, dear Don sea, created by the will of the Bolshevik Party, the will which it planted in the heart of the people of our great Mother Country, which it put into their heroic hands.

For ever greetings, Volga–Don canal, the brilliant creation of the mind and labour of the Soviet people!

Along the Volga–Don ship canal, which has been given the name of the creator of our party, of our Soviet state, the immortal name of Vladimir Ilich Lenin, caravans of vessels loaded with coal, timber, grain, machinery, paper – all the wealth of the country – are steaming along the new and mighty water artery of our Motherland.

We, contemporaries and witnesses of the start of the gigantic plan for conquering nature, are at present in a position to make only rough sketches of what we have seen. But a writer will come who will create a work worthy of the great reconstruction.

How many exploits, how many demonstrations of valour and self-sacrifice on the part of Soviet man, the peaceful builder but, when necessary, also the warrior, have been written into the story of the creation of the Volga–Don ship canal! How many sleepless nights, how many meditations, how much energy have been deposited in the mighty carcass of the Tsimlansk hydro-electric station dam, in the canal, the sluices, in all the installations of Volga–Don! And, just as the whole country participated in the preparation of the equipment, machinery and mechanisms for the Volga–Don, so all the multi-national sons and daughters of the Mother Country participated in the gigantic construction works, in transforming into life the true ideas and hopes of those who once lived among us and thought of the good of the people.

It had become a subject of everyday talk, and we had come to call the creation of the Volga–Don canal an age-old dream of the Russian people. Peter I thought about it, the foremost people of Russia thought about it; but their thoughts were fruitless. And it was not without reason that Prince Golitsin, the governor of Astrakhan, to whom Peter entrusted the direction of the works for cutting the Volga–Don canal, and who had believed fanatically in the possibility of realizing the work undertaken, wrote: 'God alone directs the course of the rivers, and it would be impertinent of man to unite that which the Almighty has sundered.'

But now people welded by the will of the Communist Party have arrived and created that which once seemed impertinent and impossible of achievement.

The dream, which in our time became the dream of all the people, has been incarnated in reality by the Bolshevik Party; and it is not without good reason, as in the Fatherland war, that in every section of the work there were hundreds of Communists.

They led the masses into the fight to master the elemental forces of nature, to create and accomplish the great national reconstruction work.

Here they are then, the creators of the vast energy which is serving the great aims of the construction of Communism.

Engineer Fiodor Ivanovich Rezchikov, the head of the fourth construction district of the Tsimlansk hydro-grid, a man from the city of Gorky, who in some respects distantly – whether in the features or in his workman's build – is reminiscent of his great fellow-countryman. Smiling, and a little moved, he tells us:

'Under me I had a brigade of some twenty men, commanded by Alyakin. He himself comes from Moldavia. The majority of the constructors in the brigade also come from there. They worked extraordinarily well, but that was not all: on the day of the high water last year, when the broken ice threatened to shatter the ice-breaks of the temporary railway bridge, they jumped down on to the ice-floes with crowbars and broke them up so as to save the bridge. They worked like sappers at the front.

'At the beginning of winter, early one morning I went down to the bank of the Don. Some ancient Cossack came up to me and asked:

' "So you're constructing, my son?"

' "Yes, daddy."

' "Well, what do you think? Will it work?"

'I answered, "If the Bolsheviks have thought of it, then it must work."

'The old man knitted his brows: "Go on building, my son. Look: the willow is red, and that means the winter will be mild. But look out in the spring: after the water breaks up the ice, warm water will follow; be on your guard against that: it will give you a bath. It's only in books that they write that the Don is gentle; when it starts to play about in the spring it's an animal! It will break down any barrier. If you don't want it to carry away what you're doing, keep a good look out with both eyes!"

'Then he turned and went.

'The break-up of the ice caused us plenty of anxiety and

trouble. It looked as though everything had been foreseen by the engineers. But the floodwater was so unexpectedly high – according to the testimony of old inhabitants the highest for the past seventy years – that only the combination of powerful technique and the heroism of our people averted an elemental disaster. Our people had no sleep for several days, but they saved the dam and the temporary bridge. The water rose up to the floor of the bridge, and the ice-breaks cracked so loud it was simply fearful. The old man proved right: when the high water set in the flood brought down brush-wood, beams, trees hewn in the Don hinterland; and the blocks set up round the bridge piles threatened a catastrophe. We broke up the ice with blasting charges; but we couldn't deal in that way with the brushwood and the trees the water had brought down. The Alyakinites, as we called the men of Alyakin's brigade, jumped down on to the blocks with axes and saws and, standing up to their waists in the madly swirling water, hewed and sawed the tree trunks and cut the brush-wood away so that they floated off, to enable the water to get away through the gaps between the piles.'

Neither Alyakin nor his comrades are working in the construction area now; but the work they did will always remain in the memory of those with whom and for whom they worked.

The greatest possible exploitation of the latest and finest techniques in the construction work by no means rendered unnecessary the application of hard physical labour, sometimes accompanied by great risk. In the high tide of last year torrents of water tore down towards the pits of the sluices and the hydro-electric station. They washed away the gravel of the roads, destroyed the bases of the earthworks building up the earth dams. In order to save the flooded works the constructors worked up to their necks in the icy water. And they did what they did without being ordered, on their own initiative and desire. They saved the right-bank section of the dam and the bulkheads of the sluice pits leading to the Tsimlansk hydro-electric station.

When, after turning the current of the Don under the over-flow weir, they filled in the old bed of the river, now dry, they had a hard job.

It was night, the darkness lit with the light of electric lamps

253

and flood lights. Thousands of people stood by the lorries. Not only the constructors themselves were there, but also the inhabitants of the local hamlets and villages, who had come to contribute their physical labour to that of those who were constructing and creating.

Glancing momentarily out of the window of the plank hut which was his command post, Rezchikov, the chief of the construction district, could not immediately be sure whether it was the excavators loading the lorries, or whether they were being filled to the brim with stones by the hands of thousands of people in a few seconds. Only sparks flew as stone struck against stone. Only eyes glittered among those who were filling in the bed of their own river in order that life might be simpler, might be easier.

And I must mention that our ciné-camera men were rather amusingly caught on the wrong foot. Calculating that it would take some sixty hours to fill the river bed, they lost the opportunity to register this historic event for the cinema, because the Don was filled in in one night, in eight hours. And when at dawn their astonished eyes surveyed the stone embankment barring off the Don, the head of the political department of the hydro-grid construction works, Alexei Gavrilovich Cherkasov, who had his own sense of humour, consoled them with hypocritical sympathy in their despair:

'Well, of course it's an outrage. They reckoned to get it done in sixty hours, but the constructors misled you: they set to work and did it in eight. But tell me what I can do to help you. Shall we take it all up and start again? It's been done thoroughly, so is it worth while destroying it? I sympathize with you, but I can't be much help in your trouble.'

The head of the construction works, Vasily Arsentievich Barabanov, stood with the engineers on the bank like a regimental commander on the field of battle, agitated, but concentrated in a tight knot of will. And the old Cossacks wept as they saw not their former Don, but a tamed river brought into the service of the people.

Here is the pleasant, simple, workman's face of the Leningrad man, Sergei Grigorievich Petrov. He has taken part in the installation of sixteen power stations, he has worked in the far north and the far south of our land, in its east and its west. He has travelled all over the country, he has spent a long working life in it, and, to tell the truth, from the human aspect he has had a pretty poor time of it. Once a year he manages to get back to his native city, to his family. But if construction work has to be done, he does it. His boys, who are attending a secondary school, are not able to change their school and transfer to wherever their nomadic father happens to be working. He gets absorbed in every construction job; every turbine set to work is his child. And today he wipes his hands with some tow, and looks at the new turbine with, possibly, his usual thought: I must get ready to go on to Takhai-Tash.

There are many, very many such skilled workmen with golden hands.

The construction works of the Volga–Don canal are to be seen as one of the great creations of the people. On its upper spur rises the greatest earthen dam in the world, thirteen kilometres of it, stretching across the Don hinterland. The beautiful hydro-electric station sends current to the industrial centres of the south and the villages of the trans-Don districts. Water is flowing along the Don canal into the heart of the arid steppes.

A miraculous ladder of locks has been built on a high watershed from the Don to the Volga rivers; over that ladder flows and flows an endless flood of commodities.

But here, on the Volga–Don, one can see only a small part of the great work which is being and will be created in our great country in the name of the people's happiness.

Not one single capitalist country can dream of such vast construction for the benefit of the people. At one time foreign engineers drew up a plan for transforming the Mediterranean Sea. They proposed to bar the Straits of Gibraltar and the Dardanelles with dams, to lower the sea level, and then enormous stretches of fertile earth would be liberated from under the water. An electric power station on the Gibraltar dam could have become a mighty source of energy, capable of transforming six million square metres of the Sahara desert into a flourishing garden. The entire work would have cost a fifteenth of the cost of the First World War. But in capitalistic conditions such construction works, bringing colossal benefits to humanity, are unrealizable. Capitalism buries the fruits of technical thought, the science and engineering of progressive minds, in the 'graveyard of plans'.

'Wherever you look,' wrote Vladimir Ilich Lenin, 'at every step you meet with tasks which humanity is quite capable of accomplishing immediately. Capitalism prevents them. It has accumulated piles of wealth – and has made people the slaves of this wealth. It has resolved the most complex problems of technique, and has prevented the application of technical improvements because of the indigence and ignorance of millions of the population, because of the stupid niggardliness of a handful of millionaires.'

A striking example of the exploiters' ruination of the toiling people is the glorified hydro-electric construction work in the United States. When the Grand Coulee hydro-electric station on the Columbia river was being constructed – and, by the way, it has been under construction for more than two decades and is still not completely finished – the avaricious traders, businessmen and state officials were by no means niggardly with their publicity on the 'coming days of gold' for the agriculture of the State of Washington. Thousands of farmers from all parts of the country rose to this bait. They rushed into 'the fertile valley' to the promised happiness, they purchased plots of land with their last resources, and became the victims of a shameless deception. As it was, the wretched earth did not see the coming of irrigation, and the ruined farmers, cursing the cunning tricks of the capitalist smarties, abandoned their barren plots and went off again to seek their spectral 'fortune'. And today the Columbia river is supplying its energy not to the soil thirsting for moisture, not to the ordinary toiling people, but to the instigators of war, the men who are preparing atom bombs for the annihilation of humanity.

Our Volga–Don is a construction work for the genuine peace and happiness of the people. It will irrigate and water two million seven hundred and fifty thousand hectares of arid soil. It will pour new energy into our vigorously developing socialistic industry, it will put in motion hundreds of electric tractors.

The construction of the Volga–Don canal involved the re-settlement of many Cossack villages and hamlets scattered over the area to be flooded. But the resettlement caused them no hurt whatever, it did not ruin them, as had happened with the farmers in the Columbia River valley. The Soviet Government showed all its fatherly care for the Cossack collective farmers, for their present and for their future.

The Cossack resettlers were given large sums of money for their houses, their farm yards, their wells, for every apple and every cherry tree in their old farmsteads. The State aided the collective farmers with transport, with building materials; it allocated them farmsteads on the banks of the sea which at that time was still uncreated.

Of course, it was not easy for the old people to abandon the spots where they had lived for so long. Before they left for their new settlement more than one of them kissed the ground on which he himself had been born, and his father, his grand-father and great-grandfather.

But it was not long before the inhabitants had settled down in their new homes, and had grown used to this young sea.

This is what happened to the village of Solenov. Today, on the spot where the village once stood, there are a dam and a hydro-electric power station; turbines are roaring, and the Solenov villagers are living not far away, right on the shore of the sea.

The village of Solenov had its long and glorious reputation. In 1918 all the Cossacks in the village went off to form a Red partisan detachment, and later they were among the first to organize a collective farm, calling it after the commander of the detachment, Chornikov, who had fallen in battle. In the years of the Great Patriotic War hundreds of Solenov Cossacks fought at the front, smashing the Nazi invaders. Later on, many of the villagers worked devotedly in the Volga–Don construction works.

The Solenov people settled next to the 'Tsimlansk Force' collective farm; and the inhabitants of Tsimlansk, who had been long settled there – the carpenters, joiners, tilers and smiths – gave brotherly help to their new neighbours.

The Solenov people transferred the remains of four famous

partisans – Alexei Chornikov, Vasily Tiorskov, Moisei Yermakov and Vasily Frolov – to the centre of their new village.

With their combined efforts they built good wooden houses for the soldier's widow Yevdokia Kurbatova, and for the war-wounded Terenty Kurochkin and Alexander Skorbatov, who until the transfer had lived in ill-favoured small huts.

The Solenov collective farm named after Chornikov has struck strong roots into its new location. Orchards are already growing on the occupied land. The trees haven't flowered yet, but they will!

Winds from the east will bend the crowns of the young apple and pear trees, the irrigated lands of the trans-Don steppe will sway with luxuriant grain, a young generation of builders of Communism will grow up to the joy of their mother country.

Installations will be constructed still more imposing, still more splendid, than the Volga–Don. But in the consciousness of the people the Volga–Don will remain the first-born of the great construction works. And – although they will not always admit it – the mothers always have a greater and more tender love for their first-born.

Dear people, on whose behalf all the plans and interests of our wise Bolshevik Party are engaged, the creator of all that which serves peace and happiness, rejoice in your great achievements!

Under the most difficult conditions of the still unfinished Civil War, imperialist intervention and ruthless destruction, the Soviet people set to work to realize the plan of that genius, Lenin, for the electrification of the country. During the first two years the capacity was only 12,000 kilowatts of electric power. The results were still extremely small. But, encouraging the people to a magnificent civic exploit, Vladimir Ilich said:

'Twelve thousand kilowatts is a very modest beginning. Maybe a foreigner acquainted with American, German or Swedish electrification will laugh at it. But he laughs best who laughs last.'

As we create this great installation we rejoice, we smile; but it is not a smile of self-satisfaction, rather the smile of the conqueror, the smile of those who look forward confidently to the coming happiness of all humanity.

1952, Tsimlansk Hydro-electric Grid

Forever Greetings, Dear Party!

With feelings of profound love and gratitude the toilers of our country note the glorious half-century of existence of the Communist Party of the Soviet Union: to which, in 1917, the people suffering under the oppression of capitalism boldly entrusted their fate, regarding the party created by the great Lenin as their unique and faithful defender, capable of realizing their age-long hopes and dreams; the party that boundlessly believes in the inviolable rightness of its general work for the nation; in its kindred and indissoluble association with them, the people – the creators and constructors of a living, longed-for future.

In the years of civil war and armed intervention this unshakable faith in their own party, born in the womb of the Russian revolutionary working class, inspired the Soviet people to exploits unexampled in history, unforgettable in their greatness. This faith raised and inspired them to overcome unheard-of difficulties in the post-war reconstruction period.

During the years of the Soviet régime the people, led by the party, and having become the genuine masters of their own land, were spiritually transformed, their social, political and cultural development was unprecedented. And so they loved their Mother Country, which had been regenerated in the revolution, in a new fashion and with yet more fire; and gathered into themselves such might as aided them in the Great Patriotic War not only to turn the Fascist aggressors to dust but to crush them to death.

In desperate, bloody battles with their enemies the Soviet people, who were trained and steeled by the party, confirmed in practice Lenin's prophetic words, uttered in 1919, to the effect that a people will never be conquered who are fighting for their Soviet régime, struggling with great sacrifices to keep the freedom they have gained, and to ensure the happy and joyous future of their children.

Peaceful labour over the decades and the blood shed abundantly in battles for the freedom and independence of their country have fused the people and the party once for all. What force can separate them now? There is no such force, and never will be in this world.

To the joy of all their friends and to the angry disillusionment of all their enemies, in the shortest time after the victorious end to the Great Patriotic War the Land of the Soviets under the leadership of the party completely restored its national economy, healed the bleeding wounds the war had inflicted on its body and became even mightier, an even stronger centripetal force for all advanced and progressive humanity.

But where are those great political figures and those thievish small fry of the Press of the imperialistic stable, who during the years of war predicted our defeat, and avidly awaited it, with a shiver of joy? Where are the ill-starred soothsayers who, after German Fascism was shattered, incessantly ventriloquized with bestial roars and howls that the Soviet Union had been flung a long way back by the war and that many decades would be needed to restore its ruined economy, and also undoubtedly the aid of capitalistic powers? Strange to say, they are not to be seen or heard; and one has no idea where, in what indecent spot they are hiding their eyes shamelessly corrupted, filmed with hatred for the land of socialism. The firm, frank and clear gaze of the peace-loving Soviet people has no desire to meet those delirious eyes of human rabble and filth. It is fixed calmly and confidently on the future, on our longed-for morrow.

All the works, all the strivings and plans of the party and its central committee are directed today towards the further strengthening of the economic might and the defence potential of the motherland, towards the preservation and consolidation of peace all over the world, towards an even greater and steadily increasing rise in the toilers' living standards. They are directed towards ensuring that through the accelerated development of the country's productive forces and the mass introduction of first-class technique into the production processes there will be an all-round lightening of physical labour, which still only recently laid a heavy burden on the shoulders of the people, who indeed had had to work very hard in their time, but who as always, as from of old, remain granite-hard and with a vast scope in their labour.

How can the people not love a party and not follow a party which for half a century has sacredly defended and protected their vital interests, has taught vigilance and always speaks to them with the simple and manly voice of truth? How can the people not love a party and not follow a party to whom care for the well-being and happiness of the people is the supreme law? And the people whole-heartedly love their own party, they believe in its brilliant, collective intelligence, and are ready always, with all their powers and to the very end, to support all its activity and labour.

From the radiant heights of the victories achieved on a universal historical scale the Soviet people look back with just pride on the heroic road they have traversed, with their party bearing the banner at their head. They know that there is much they have yet to accomplish, much yet to experience of adversities and difficulties in order to achieve the final objective: the construction of a Communist society. But, confident in their titanic might and the inexhaustible strength of the Communist Party, their collective leader and foremost force, they gaze majestically into the future, where complete victory awaits them.

Then for ever greetings, dear party, fearless and unaging in labours and exploits.

1953

A Letter to Naval Men

Dear friends, men of the navy!

Many thanks for your warm letter and for your interest in my creative work.

You ask why I made Davidov a Baltic sailor.

There were several prototypes for Davidov. I have met many sailors, and talked with them, and seen how they work in the sphere to which the party has directed them. And everywhere they have contributed their fine naval revolutionary traditions to life.

Vladimir Ilich Lenin paid a high tribute to the sailors after the events of October. And they fought just as splendidly in the Civil War; they took a very active part in the building up of the Soviet regime.

And it was this that gave me the idea of making Davidov a former Baltic sailor. For a man who went to work in the villages had to be possessed of courage, steadfastness, good humour, the ability to handle people, to feel the sense of the collective. All these qualities, with unswerving devotion to the party and the cause of Communism, I saw in the sailors trained in our fleet.

That, I think, is all I can say briefly in reply to your letter.

I send you warm greetings, dear glorious sailors, on the occasion of the glorious fortieth anniversary of our Armed Forces.

1958

Concerning Semion Davidov

(From a speech at the Kirov works, Leningrad)

Dear friends, Kirov workers. I am often asked why the hero of *Virgin Soil Upturned*[1], Semion Davidov, was a worker at the Putilov, now the Kirov works, and before that had been a Baltic sailor.

More than thirty years ago, when I was still a young writer, I chose this way of expressing my profound respect for the foremost working class, that of 'Peter', for its glorious revolutionary deeds and traditions. It was my first low bow to the Leningrad workers, and especially to those of the Kirov works.

My second bow was to the glorious sailors of the Baltic fleet, with my equally profound respect for its deeds and revolutionary traditions.

I am proud that I made Semion Davidov, the hero of *Virgin Soil Upturned*, the organizer and chairman of a collective farm in our Don country, a man from among you, that he is your son. . . .

And how fine it is now to see the new generation, who owe so much to Semion Davidov and his contemporaries for their experience and training, and who have become the inheritors of their finest traditions!

I and my fellow Don countrymen have come on this visit to you, dear Kirov workers, not only to talk about our affairs, but also to invite you to come and visit us on the Don. Come and take a look at the life which flourishes in the area where Semion Davidov, the former Putilov worker, gave his life.

1961

[1] Published in America as *Seeds of Tomorrow*.

Now This is Something!

*(On the flight of the first cosmonaut,
Yuri Gagarin)*

Now this really is something!
And there's nothing more to say, since one is dumb with admiration and pride at the fantastic success of the science of our native fatherland.

Vioshenska, April 11th, 1961

I give you a strong, Fatherly Hug

(On the flight of Valentina Tereshkova and
Valery Bikovsky into the cosmos)

I realize that what I have to say on this day of triumph may sound a jarring note. But now can I help it? My elderly years and somewhat conservative cast of mind had until the last few days compelled me to think that we men were both the 'lords of thought' and the warriors, and that altogether we were the salt of the earth in this sub-lunar world.

But now what has happened? A woman in the cosmos? Well, I don't care what you say, this is beyond all understanding. It contradicts all my settled views of the world and its possibilities. I would gladly hug Valery Bikovsky for his exploit – that's what he's a man for, to achieve exploits. But the situation is quite different in regard to Valentina Vladimirovna Tereshkova.

Now she is being overwhelmed with thousands of offers of hand and heart; but I, having borne the cross of married life for forty years, cannot offer her either my hand or my heart. But I give her a strong, fatherly hug and wish her all the very best in life. And it goes without saying that I hug and kiss dear Valery Fiodorovich Bikovsky.

Vioshenska (undated)

To Serve the People with Integrity

(Speech at a Conference of Writers
of the European Community)

I have been given the high honour of welcoming you, the outstanding writers of Europe, in the name of the Union of Soviet Writers, and to wish you success in the work of your conference.

Here, with the exception of the ladies, I see mainly elderly men, writers and critics, undoubtedly burdened both with worldly and with literary experience. And so we won't be naïve: I have been granted this high honour, of being the first to welcome you, not out of respect for my grey hairs, not in recognition of my literary services, but because my friend Aliosha Surkov and the other leading workers in the Union of Soviet Writers know me as a cocky, argumentative person. And so they decided: 'We'll get Sholokhov to be the first Soviet writer to speak; he'll welcome our dear guests, and then it will be inconvenient for him to get up and make critical remarks after they've spoken.'

So diplomacy has been at work here too. But it happens to correspond with my own mood: it is much easier to say pleasant than unpleasant things to a man.

But all the same, I'd like to reserve myself the right to speak, if during the conference they start planing the boards and getting the coffin ready in order to bury the novel.

For me personally the question of the novel's 'to be or not to be' simply doesn't arise, any more than a peasant is faced with the question whether or not to sow grain.

His problem can be put along the following lines: 'How to sow and how to cultivate a better harvest.'

And in exactly the same way for me, as a novelist, the question can arise: how to write a novel better, so that it may serve my people, my readers, with integrity.

But we'll start talking about that during the business part of the conference.

We begin our conference on an outstanding day. Today an agreement for the banning of nuclear tests will be signed in Moscow. I reflect that the great political leaders and diplomats have reached agreement. So surely we, writers, will manage to reach agreement on how best to serve man and the cause of peace with our art. Otherwise we shall be put to shame before our readers. We've simply got to find a common language, and without doubt it will be found!

We Soviet writers welcome you, our dear guests, with open heart and expansive Russian hospitality.

All the conditions requisite to our work have already been created. It is good that the conference is being held in Leningrad. Here it is cooler than in Moscow. But if the polemics take too fiery a turn we can transfer the conference, say to Archangel or Murmansk. In a word, to any place, so long as our talk about the novel is moderate, judicious and yields good results.

We hope that the conference will prove of value, and your stay in our country pleasant.

August 5, 1963, Leningrad

Inaugural Speech at the Second Congress of Writers of the R.S.F.S.R.

Comrades!

I have been entrusted with a very honourable and responsible task: to open the second Congress of Writers in the Russian lands.

I do it with a feeling of joy and even emotion, for I realize that today the attention of millions of people both in our country and beyond its borders is centred on this hall, where the representatives of the great Russian and the many other notable literatures, developing all over the expanse of Russia, are gathered.

I am quite sure that the work of our congress will not go unremarked by the world community and, in particular, by the Press. Of course, we must be ready for comments not only from friends who sincerely rejoice in our successes and feel pain with our pains; for undoubtedly our non-friends will wish to comment on our work. I have in mind those gentlemen who don't want to be fed with bread but will want to talk slanderously about our labours.

Well, God be with them, with our foreign commentators. We have an inexhaustible range of matters which we must discuss in this congress frankly and in a businesslike fashion. So that our people, our many millions of readers, may not wonder why these writers left their places of work – their writing desks – and occupied themselves with things that are not in their line at all: conferences, when we already have too many conferences in our country.

But the people's opinion is what we writers ought to value above all else in the world. For how can the life and work of every one of us be justified if not by the trust of the people, if not by the recognition that he is devoting all his strength and capacities to the people, the party, the Mother Country?

I think it is precisely here that we need to seek the key to the problem of the creative intelligentsia in the life of our society. If, indeed, such a problem exists at all. . . . It sometimes seems to me, much as I regret having to say it, that we make far too much of this problem. Of course it's pleasant when people treat you with care, help you, find good words to say of you. But surely is not every one of us of the Soviet intelligentsia, who have been fed and watered by the party and the people, bound in his turn to treat everything which has been won in this very difficult half-century of struggle which has involved all of us – all our people, our party, our native Soviet régime – with profound love and filial care?

If I were to be asked my personal opinion, I should say that the problem of the intelligentsia is resolved so far as we are concerned fairly simply: be a faithful soldier of the Leninist party, no matter whether you're Communist or non-party; give all of yourself, all your strength, all your soul to the people; live one life with them, share with them in their joys and difficulties – there you have the whole 'problem'!

You and we are faced with spending several days together here in Moscow. And not simply to spend them, but to work, and to work intensively. And so that these days may pass with the greatest benefit to our common cause, to Soviet literature, let's agree in advance: our work will be done in a friendly spirit, as it should be among comrades of the same regiment, who have one aim, one care. Let's try to put aside all petty affronts and misunderstandings. Let that which unites us all be foremost in our minds: care for the further successes of our great Soviet literature. That is what the party greatly expects from us, what all the people greatly expect from us.

I think you'll understand me aright: I'm not calling for general forgiveness and kisses all round. Friendship is friendship; but in our literary, our ideological work certain principles are involved, retreat from which may not be forgiven even your close friend. Only then will our unity be firm when we do not close our eyes to one another's mistakes, when we learn to call things by their right names. If there is anything in our midst which hinders literature from working normally, developing normally, let's ruthlessly take note of it. If there are still some among us who are not averse at times from flirting with their liberalism, from playing at 'give-away' in the ideological struggle, let's tell them to their faces that we're thinking about it.

Too great a responsibility rests on your and my shoulders, too great and precious a task has been entrusted to us, for us to depart from frank party conversation.

Of course, every one of us has his painful problems, every one of those who speak will undoubtedly feel a desire to touch upon them, to talk about the work and cares of his comrades in the literary organization. But how important it is for us – and allow me to put special emphasis on this – always to keep before our eyes the main orientation, our main theme – literature and the life of the people, literature and the construction of Communism. If you and we manage to keep on this high note, then the result will be a song, and our congress will become not simply a routine literary enterprise, but a lofty and fruitful gathering of people seriously thinking over life, over our art.

Abroad we are often asked, sometimes with a sneer, sometimes with a sincere desire to understand, to explain, to give a popular exposition, so to speak, of Socialist realism. I shall not risk taking bread from the mouths of our theoreticians, and, like any practitioner, I'm not very strong on scientific formulations. But I usually answer these questions in this way: Socialist realism is the art of the truth of life, the truth understood and conceived by the artist from the position of Leninist partisanship. Or, if it needs to be put even more simply, then in my view the art which actively helps people in the construction of a new world – *is* the art of Socialist realism.

Anyone who wishes to understand what Socialist realism is should closely examine the enormous experience of Soviet literature during the all but half-century of its existence. The history of that literature *is* Socialist realism, incarnated in the living images of heroes and the living pictures of the national struggle.

May the sublime road traversed during this half-century by Soviet literature and, in particular, by one of its leading detachments, Russian literature, be present before our eyes today, as we think together over the morrow of art. We have a tremendous treasure behind us. We have something to be proud of, we have something to oppose to vociferous but barren abstractionism. And although we see how much we still have to do in order to justify the people's trust, although by and large we are still dissatisfied with our work, all the same we must never forget how much has been contributed by our literature to the spiritual treasury of mankind, how great and indisputable is its authority in all the world.

Dear comrades! The writers of the Russian Federation are the first in our country to assemble in their congress. It is, so to speak, the first swallow among the congresses of the various republics. It would be fine if we, Russians, carry on our great conversation about literature with respect to principles in a businesslike and exacting manner. I think that we and you will succeed in doing just that.

With the expression of this hope, allow me to declare the Second Congress of Writers of the Russian Federation open.

(Undated)

Mikhail Sholokhov was born in 1905 in a village in the Don region. His parents were poor, but they managed to send him to school in Moscow. At the age of fifteen he returned to his native village to become a schoolteacher, then a statistician, a food inspector, and half a dozen other things. He and his father were the only men in the town, and there in those bloody years 1920–3 he saw with his own eyes what civil war meant.

He began writing when he was eighteen years old and is today one of the most popular writers in the Soviet Union—literally millions of copies of his works have been sold.

He still lives in the country of his forefathers on the Don, where he has a small farm with a few head of cattle. When he is not writing, he spends his leisure fishing and hunting; but there is not much leisure for him, for he is greatly in demand for lectures and other public work.

In 1938 he was chosen a deputy to the Supreme Soviet of the U.S.S.R. and a member of the Academy of Sciences and of the Presidium Union of Soviet Writers. In 1941 he received the Stalin Prize for Literature, carrying a sum equivalent to $28,000, and he has twice been awarded the Order of Lenin. Regarded as a Soviet national hero, Sholokhov has nonetheless continually asserted in his writings and in his often blunt challenges to the Soviet's literary dictators his independence of the official Communist viewpoint. Thus he was one of the few writers in Russia to defend Boris Pasternak during the controversy over the publication of *Dr. Zhivago*. In 1965 he was awarded the Nobel Prize for Literature for the "artistic power and integrity with which, in his epic of the Don, he has given creative expression to a historic phase in the history of the Russian people."

*The text of this book was set overseas in the typeface Imprint.
The book was printed by Halliday Lithograph Corp.,
West Hanover, Mass., and bound by The Book Press Inc.,
Brattleboro, Vt.*